Godly Relationships

By

Kaye Freeman

**"I no longer call you servants, because a servant does not know his master's business. Instead, I have called you friends, for everything that I learned from my Father I have made known to you"
John 15:15.**

ISBN: 0-9703069-8-9

Book cover and layout: John Owen

Editors: Marilyn Price
          Emily Freeman
          Darlene Arkison

Published by: Train-Up A Child Publishing, L.L.C.
                 PO Box 1122
                 Jenks, Ok 74037

Website: www.trainupstudies.com

Endorsements

"My daughter really enjoyed doing the lessons. She looked forward to doing them, and I didn't even have to prompt her! I would recommend the Train-Up Studies to all homeschooling parents who want to get their children firmly grounded in the Word."

Jerrylene Birchett, Homeschooling Mom, Tulsa, OK

"Today, at every turn, our children are bombarded with a naturalistic world view that says that they are a product of science and not from a Heavenly Father who created and loves them. State adopted textbooks, library books and television tell our children they come from nature. In order to teach our children to stand against the tide, it is necessary that we as parents and teachers give them a solid Biblical foundation.

Kaye Freeman's fresh new curriculum is comprehensive and gives children a firm foundation in God's Word. The Train-Up Studies will help a child to grow spiritually and stand against the enemy. Its straightforward format is easy to implement for any parent or teacher."

Nancy Huff, Teach the Children Ministries, Tulsa, OK

"Kaye Freeman has developed a Bible curriculum that is not only spiritually strong but also educationally sound. Her lesson format incorporates many principles of good teaching such as previewing and reviewing of material, varied question formats, emphasizing comprehension and providing opportunities throughout the studies for children to interact with the text. These Bible study lessons are a blessing to children of any age."

Gina Johnson, Education Therapist, Tulsa, OK

"Thank God for Kaye Freeman's fresh new curriculum. Every child needs to go through the Train-Up Studies. The lessons are age relevant, easy to understand and are a wonderful guide for any parent or teacher to use to teach a child to understand God's Word and make the right choices."

Rod Baker, Director of Children's Ministry Department
Victory Christian Center, Tulsa, OK

About the Author

Kaye Freeman is a wife and a homeschooling mother. She is a graduate of Oklahoma State University. She and her husband, Don, have two children, Emily and Caleb. Attending Victory Bible Institute, Kaye is a part-time student in the Biblical Studies Program. Additionally, Kaye teaches 7th and 8th grade Bible and writing classes at C.E.A., which is a homeschool co-op, where Emily and Caleb attend classes three days a week.

Several years ago, Kaye began writing Bible studies for her children to do at home. Now, she writes studies for children and teens all over the world. Her vision is to disciple them in the things of Christ—to train them up in the way they should go.

As a child, Kaye faced physical challenges. By the age of 18, she was undergoing her second heart surgery. At that time, she did not know that God is a healing God and that His plans for her future were for good and not for evil. It wasn't until she was an adult that Kaye discovered this wonderful truth about her Lord and Savior. Now she's determined to teach children and teens everywhere the truth about God through the Train-Up A Child Bible Studies.

Website: www.trainupstudies.com

Table of Contents

Lesson 1

Defining a Relationship

Welcome to this study, *Godly Relationships*. Over the next 16 lessons, you will learn the definition of a godly relationship and that God is the originator of relationships. You'll discover that two of God's greatest commandments are centered on relationships. Examining relationships that He established with people in the Bible, you'll discover how you can become God's friend. Additionally, you will learn the steps to developing and strengthening your relationship with Him.

According to God, choosing godly friends is vital. In His Word, He provides instruction regarding how to treat a friend once you've established a friendship. Throughout this workbook, you'll discover His advice. Unsurprisingly, God even addresses boy/girl relationships in His Word. You'll find out what He has to say about them, too. Finally, you'll learn the characteristics of a godly person and the importance of being godly in an ungodly world. Are you ready to get started?

The first order of business is to define the word "relationship." What does this word mean to you? In the space provided below, write your answer.

1. _____

_____

_____

A relationship is a connection between two or more parties who share a common bond. Perhaps they are in the same family or share the same likes or dislikes. Maybe they share the same beliefs spiritually. Whatever the connection may be, it is strong enough to form a bond between them.

A relationship can be weak or strong. There are a number of factors that determine the strength of a relationship. One fact is certain. A relationship requires a commitment from both parties if it is going to be successful and strong. Caring for one another, each person must put forth the effort and the time it takes to build and maintain a strong relationship.

Have you ever wondered, *Why did God create man?* The Bible reveals several reasons why God created people. Turning to the verses listed below, read each one. If there is an (OT) beside the verse, it is found in the Old Testament. If there is an (NT) beside it, it is found in the New Testament. Beside each verse, list the reason(s) given for God's creation of man.

2. Genesis 1:28 (OT): _____

_____

_____

_____

_____

3. Genesis 2:5 (OT): _____

4. Isaiah 43:7 (OT): _____

5. Ephesians 2:10 (NT): _____

_____

6. Colossians 1:16 (NT): _____

_____

From the verses you just read, you discovered that God created man to have children, or be fruitful, and to multiply. Creating man to inhabit and care for the earth, God intended for him to take dominion over all that He had created. Additionally, God created man for His (God's) glory. Daily, we are to glorify God in all that we say and do.

Ephesians 2:10 states that God created man to do good works. When you show love and kindness toward others, you are demonstrating God's love for them. God is glorified in this.

Colossians 1:16 says that God created man for Himself. Certainly, God did not need to create man. He chose to. One of the most important reasons why God created man was because He desires to have a relationship with us.

After placing the first man, Adam, in the Garden of Eden, God said, **"It is not good for the man to be alone. I will make a helper suitable for him"** Genesis 2:18 (OT). Causing Adam to fall into a deep sleep, God removed one of his ribs. From it, God formed woman. Adam called her Eve. God saw that all He had created was good.

For a time, God walked with Adam and Eve in the Garden. They spent time together. They communicated with each other. God provided all that Adam and Eve needed. In return, He commanded that they obey Him. What a wonderful beginning! Unfortunately, it didn't last long.

What interferes with our relationship with God? What separates us from Him? Certainly there are a number of distractions in this world that interfere with our relationship with the Lord. Sin is undoubtedly the greatest factor that separates man from God. Sin is exactly what came between Adam, Eve and God in the Garden of Eden.

Disguising himself as a snake, Satan suggested to Eve that she disobey God by eating from the tree God had commanded her not to eat. After Eve took a bite of the forbidden fruit, she encouraged Adam to do the same. He did. Their disobedience brought about separation from God and eventually death.

Lovingly, God did not give up on establishing relationships with people. Throughout the Old Testament, He developed relationships with Noah, Abraham, Isaac and Jacob. Additionally, God established relationships with Joseph, Moses, Joshua and David. You will study about some of those relationships in the lessons that follow.

Unfortunately, man's disobedience continued to separate him from God. Fortunately, God performed the miraculous when He sent His Son, Jesus, to bridge the gap between Himself and man. Residing on the earth for 33 years, Jesus set the standard for developing and maintaining good relationships. At the young age of 33, He paid the ultimate price, which was His blood, in order to restore man's relationship with God that was so carelessly lost in the Garden of Eden.

God loves you. The Bible says that if you believe and confess Jesus as Lord and Savior of your life, then you are a child of God. Nothing can compare to the love that God has for His children. God is your Father, and He longs to have a relationship with you.

How do you develop a relationship with God? There are three important steps in this process. They are:

Step 1:   Spending time with God through:
a. Studying, meditating and confessing His Word;
b. Communicating with Him through prayer;
c. Praising Him.

Step 2:   Loving God with all your heart, soul and mind.

Step 3:   Obeying God.

Over the next several lessons, you will study closely each step. As you do so, your relationship with God will become stronger.

That's enough for today. Let's review what you've learned:

- God created man to multiply; to inhabit, care for and take dominion over the earth and all that is in it; to glorify Him; to do good works, and for His sake.

- God created man in order to have a relationship with Him.

- The steps to developing and strengthening a relationship with God are: spending time with Him; loving Him with all your heart, soul and mind, and obeying Him.

This week's memory verse is Revelation 4:11 (NT). It is printed below. Say it to yourself three times.

"You are worthy, our Lord and God, to receive glory and honor and power, for you created all things, and by your will they were created and have their being."

7.   Write this verse in the space provided below.

_____

_____

_____

_____

Lesson 2

Spending Time with God

Developing and maintaining a good relationship with someone is impossible unless you spend time with that person. The more time you spend with someone, the better you get to know him or her, and the better he or she gets to know you. It's no different with God. The Bible says that God knew you before you were even born, but how much do you really know about Him? You may have heard others speak about Him. Unfortunately, you can't always believe everything that someone says about God. You must discover for yourself who God really is.

The best way to get to know God is through His Word, the Bible. Did you know that God and His Word are synonymous? "Synonymous" means the same. In his Gospel, John writes about this. Turning to John 1:1-18 (NT), read this passage titled, "The Word Became Flesh."

Below are several statements related to the passage you just read. Put a "T" in front of those statements that are true. Put an "F" in front of those statements that are false.

_____ 1. In the beginning, the Word was with God.

_____ 2. The Word was God.

_____ 3. Through the Word, all things were created.

_____ 4. Shining in the darkness, the Word was the light of men.

_____ 5. The darkness understood the Word.

_____ 6. John the Baptist was sent to testify that the true light was coming into the world.

_____ 7. The Word was sent to His own people.

___ **8.** His people recognized and received the Word.

___ **9.** To all who believe, the Word gives the right to become children of God.

___ **10.** Becoming flesh, the Word dwelt among us.

___ **11.** The Word is full of grace and truth.

___ **12.** Jesus Christ is the Word, and through Him, we can know God!

According to John, Jesus and God's Word are one and the same. Existing since the beginning of time, Jesus came to earth and lived among His people, the people of Israel. Performing numerous miracles, Jesus preached about the importance of loving God and others. While on earth, Jesus revealed the true nature of God. If you study about Jesus in God's Word, you can actually get to know God because Jesus came to do the will of the Father. Through your faith and acceptance of Christ as the true Messiah, you are made right with God and become His child.

John wrote so much more about the significance that God's Word plays in our lives. Turning over a few chapters to John 15:5-17 (NT), read these verses from the passage titled, "The Vine and the Branches." Keep in mind that this is Jesus speaking to His followers.

Following are several statements related to the passage you just read. Put a "T" in front of those statements that are true. Put an "F" in front of those statements that are false.

___ **13.** In this passage, Jesus refers to Himself as "the vine" and to His followers as "the branches."

___ **14.** Apart from Jesus, we can do all things.

___ **15.** Those who do not remain in Christ bear much fruit.

___ **16.** If you remain in Christ and His words remain in you, you may ask whatever you wish, and it will be given to you.

_____ **17.** Jesus commanded that we remain in His love.

_____ **18.** Jesus said that those who obey His commands remain in darkness.

_____ **19.** When we obey God's Word, or Jesus, our joy is complete.

_____ **20.** Jesus commanded His followers to love one another.

Jesus said that you are to abide, or remain, in Him. How do you do that? If Jesus is the Word, then you remain or abide in Him by remaining or abiding in His Word. You are to study, meditate, confess and obey His Word every day. When you do so, you bear the fruit of the Spirit listed in Galatians 5:22-23 (NT). The fruit of the Spirit is love, joy, peace, patience, kindness, goodness, faithfulness, gentleness and self-control.

In addition to bearing fruit, Jesus also promises that your joy will be complete if you abide in Him. When you abide in His Word, you can ask whatever you want, and it will be done for you. If you are abiding in God's Word, you will ask for those things that are His will for your life because His Word transforms you into the image of Christ. Lastly and most importantly, Jesus said that if you abide in Him, God will be glorified. You'll remember from Lesson 1 that one of the reasons God created you is so that He might be glorified through you. All the pieces fit perfectly together when you live your life the way God intended for you to live it.

You've taken in a great deal of information in this lesson. Hopefully, you now realize the importance of spending time with God each day by studying, meditating, confessing and obeying His Word. To meditate on God's Word means to think about it. There is no greater way to get to know God than to spend time in His Word.

Spending time with God is the first step to developing and maintaining a relationship with Him. In addition to being in His Word, you can spend time with God through prayer, praise and worship. We'll study about these methods of spending time with God in Lessons 3 and 4. See you there!

That's enough for today. Let's review what you've learned:

- Jesus is referred to as the "Word" in the Bible.
- From the very beginning, Jesus was with God.
- The Word became flesh and dwelt among man.
- Through studying God's Word, you can get to know God and Jesus.
- By remaining in God's Word, you remain in Jesus.
- Those who remain in Christ will bear much fruit.
- Jesus said that obedience is the evidence of love toward Him.

This week's memory verse is Revelation 4:11 (NT). It is printed below. Say it to yourself three times.

"You are worthy, our Lord and God, to receive glory and honor and power, for you created all things, and by your will they were created and have their being."

21. Write this verse in the space provided below.

_____

_____

_____

_____

Lesson 3

Prayer

Without communication, it's impossible to maintain a successful relationship. It's no different with God. Unless you are listening and speaking to Him on a continual basis, you cannot develop and maintain a strong relationship with the Lord. Prayer is the key to communicating with God.

Throughout the Bible, there are many verses concerning the importance of prayer. When Jesus was on the earth, He taught His followers how to pray. In this lesson, you'll learn what He taught them. Turning in your Bible to Luke 11:1-4 (NT), read these verses from the passage titled, "Jesus' Teaching on Prayer." Answer the questions that follow by writing your answers in the spaces provided.

1.   According to Jesus (verse 2), what should the first words of your prayer accomplish?

_____

_____

"Hallowed" means to honor. Praising God because He is wonderful and holy is one manner in which you can honor His name.

2.   After you have honored God in your prayer, Jesus said you should pray that God's kingdom come. What do you think He meant by that?

_____

_____

_____

When you pray that God's kingdom come, you are praying that His will be done on earth and in your life.

3.   In verse 3, for what did Jesus say you should ask?

_____

Each day when you pray, ask God to give you the necessities, which will get you through that day.

4.   For what did Jesus say you should ask God's forgiveness? According to verse 4, what specific act on your part is directly related to this request?

_____

_____

When you pray, ask God to forgive you for any sin you may have committed since the last time you prayed. Be specific. In other words, if you are aware of a specific sin you have committed, ask God to forgive you for that sin. Name it. Once you ask for His forgiveness, your slate with God is clean. However, to be forgiven, you must forgive others for any sins committed against you. According to the Bible, if you don't forgive others, God cannot forgive you.

5.   Also in verse 4, what is the fifth and final request that Jesus said you should make when you pray?

_____

Ask God to lead you and keep you from temptation because temptation leads to sin. Let's review what Jesus taught concerning prayer.

- ❖ Pray to God, and honor His name.
- ❖ Pray that God's kingdom come (or His will be done) in your life.
- ❖ Ask Him to supply your needs.
- ❖ Ask Him to forgive your sins just as you forgive others who have sinned against you.
- ❖ Ask God to lead you away from temptation.

There you have it—a guideline for prayer—straight from Jesus Himself. Of course, you don't want to pray repetitive prayers. When you do that, you are not praying from your heart. You're simply repeating words that you've memorized. Pray from the heart, but remember to pray according to Jesus' instruction. After all, He is the expert! Additionally, pray to God in Jesus' name. In John 15:16b (NT), Jesus taught this, too. Turning there, read this verse.

6. Beginning with the word "Then, " write John 15:16b (NT) in the space below.

_____

_____

Prayer is a two-way form of communication. You speak to God, and He speaks to you. How does God speak to you? He speaks to you in several ways. Probably the most common way that God will speak to you is through His Word, the Bible. Although the Bible was written many years ago, it is still the Word of God. It never changes.

Through His Holy Spirit, God will speak to you. If you're a Christian, the Holy Spirit is your conscience. He will guide you with a peace when you are moving in the right direction. He will convict you when you are not.

God will also speak to you through other believers. He may very well give another believer a special word for you. There are many examples of this in the Bible.

In a voice that you can hear either aloud or just within your spirit, God can also speak to you. Don't ever be afraid to hear from God. He loves you, and He wants to guide you down the right path.

Now that you know how to hear from God, don't forget to be listening for Him to answer your prayer. Hearing from Almighty God is a blessing and privilege that you don't want to miss.

That's enough for today. Let's review what you've learned.

- Jesus said when you pray, you should:

  ❖ Pray to God, and honor His name.
  ❖ Pray that God's will or His kingdom come in your life.
  ❖ Ask Him to supply your needs.
  ❖ Ask Him to forgive your sins just as you forgive others who have sinned against you.
  ❖ Ask Him to lead you away from temptation.

- Don't forget to end your prayer in Jesus' name.

- God will speak to you in several ways: through His Word, by His Holy Spirit, through other believers and by speaking to you Himself.

This week's memory verse is Revelation 4:11 (NT). It is printed below. Say it to yourself three times.

"You are worthy, our Lord and God, to receive glory and honor and power, for you created all things, and by your will they were created and have their being."

7. Write this verse in the space provided below.

_____

_____

_____

_____

Lesson 4

Praising and Worshipping God

In lesson 2 you learned that spending time in God's Word is one of the best ways to develop and strengthen your relationship with Him. In Lesson 3, you studied about the importance of spending time with God in prayer. Discovering that prayer is a two-way communication, you now know that you speak to God, and He speaks to you. In today's lesson, you'll learn that daily praise and worship is another important aspect in your spending time with God. Through it, you can truly experience His presence.

Have you ever experienced the presence of God? Did you even know that you could experience His presence? Writing about this very topic, the Psalmist, in Psalm 100 (OT), penned that entering into God's presence is accomplished through praise and worship. Turning in your Bible to this psalm, read it. Fill in the blanks below.

1. **"Shout for joy to the Lord, all the earth. _____ the Lord with gladness; _____ before him with joyful songs. Know that the Lord is God. It is he who made us, and we are his; we are his people, the sheep of his pasture.**

2. **_____ his gates with thanksgiving and his courts with _____; give thanks to him and _____ his name. For the Lord is good and his love endures forever; his faithfulness continues through all generations."**

In the Old Testament days, when this psalm was written, the people of Israel worshipped at the temple. Divided into three parts, the temple consisted of the outer courtyard, the Holy Place and the Most Holy Place. Those who entered into the outer courtyard did so through the gates. These are the gates to which the Psalmist was referring in the passage you just read.

The presence of God dwelt in the Most Holy Place of the temple. Once a year, the high priest prepared to enter into the Most Holy Place. Offering sacrifices to God for the sins of the people, it was the high priest's responsibility to make intercession for them. During this time, he experienced the very presence of God. This experience was not to be taken lightly or for granted.

When Jesus died on the cross, the miraculous occurred in the temple. Splitting from top to bottom, the curtain that separated the Holy Place from the Most Holy Place was torn in two. God's presence left the temple that day. Never again would He dwell in a man-made building. Now that Jesus had sacrificed His life for the sins of all men, God could live inside His people rather than among them. Although anyone who believed and confessed Jesus as Lord could now experience the presence of God, the means of experiencing God's presence did not change. Through praise and worship, you can enter into and experience God's presence.

Following are different methods prescribed in the Bible for praising and worshipping God. Look up each verse, and match it to the description listed by writing the correct letter beside each numbered verse.

____ **3.**	Psalm 33:1 (OT)	**A.**	play instruments
____ **4.**	Psalm 33:2 (OT)	**B.**	dance
____ **5.**	Psalm 33:3 (OT)	**C.**	sing joyfully
____ **6.**	Psalm 47:1 (OT)	**D.**	lift up your holy hands
____ **7.**	Psalm 63:4 (OT)	**E.**	clap your hands
____ **8.**	Psalm 95:6 (OT)	**F.**	bow or kneel down before Him
____ **9.**	Psalm 150:4 (OT)	**G.**	shout for joy

Knowing now that you can enter into God's presence and how to do so, it's time to put into practice what you have learned. Make a commitment today to praise and worship the Lord every day, and don't be surprised when God's presence comes to visit you!

That's enough for today. Let's review what you've learned:

- You can spend time with God through praise and worship.

- It is possible to experience the presence of God.

- Ways to experience God's presence and spend time with Him include:

  a. singing joyfully
  b. playing instruments
  c. shouting for joy
  d. lifting up holy hands
  e. clapping your hands
  f. dancing
  g. bowing or kneeling down before Him

This week's memory verse is Revelation 4:11 (NT). It is printed below. Say it to yourself three times.

"You are worthy, our Lord and God, to receive glory and honor and power, for you created all things, and by your will they were created and have their being."

10.   Write this verse in the space provided below.

_____

_____

_____

_____

It's time to take Test 1.

Lesson 5

Loving God

In Lesson 1, you learned that God created man to multiply, inhabit, care for and take dominion over the earth and all that is in it. Creating man to do good works, God also crafted man to glorify Him. Perhaps the most important reason that God created man, however, was because He desired to have a relationship with him.

Unfortunately, Adam and Eve chose to disobey God and, as a result, gravely affected their relationship with Him. Sin separated them from God. Fortunately, God did not give up on having a relationship with man. Throughout the Old Testament, there are countless stories of relationships that God entered into with people. Sadly, man's decision to continually disobey God resulted in separation from the Father. Many years later, God sent Jesus Christ to redeem mankind and restore man's relationship with Him. Love is the reason He did so.

During His ministry, Jesus demonstrated what God is really like. Although He was kind and compassionate to people, Jesus was adamant about the importance of obeying the Lord. One day, a Pharisee asked Jesus a very important question. Turning in your Bible to Matthew 22:34-40 (NT), read this passage titled, "The Greatest Commandment." Answer the questions that follow by placing a check mark beside the correct answer.

1.   What question did the expert in the law ask Jesus?

      a.   "Which is the greatest commandment in the Law?"
      b.   "Which is the least greatest commandment in the Law?"
      c.   "Who are more important, the Sadducees or the Pharisees?"

2.   What was the expert in the law really trying to do?

  ___   a.   learn which was the greatest commandment in the law
  ___   b.   test Jesus
  ___   c.   test the Sadducees

3.   What is the first and greatest commandment according to Jesus?

  ___   a.   "Love your neighbor as yourself."
  ___   b.   "Love yourself as much as you love God and your neighbor."
  ___   c.   "Love the Lord your God with all your heart, with all your soul and with all your mind."

4.   According to Jesus, what is the second greatest commandment?

  ___   a.   "Love your neighbor as yourself."
  ___   b.   "Love yourself as much as you love God and your neighbor."
  ___   c.   "Love the Lord your God with all your heart, with all your soul and with all your mind."

According to Jesus, all the commandments of God are centered on loving God with all your heart, soul and mind and loving others as much as you love yourself. Loving God should sound familiar to you. In Lesson 1, you discovered that loving God is one of the steps to developing and maintaining a relationship with Him. What does "love" mean?

5.   Write what you think "love" means in the space below.

_____

_____

Unsurprisingly, God defines "love" in His Word. Turning to 1 Corinthians 13:4-8a(NT), read this passage. How are you doing in the "love" department? To see, answer the questions that follow. Be honest with yourself and with God.

	Yes	**No**

Are you patient with God and others? ___ ___

 Are you kind to others? ___ ___

Do you ever find yourself wanting what
others have? ___ ___

Do you brag? (Someone who brags talks
about how great he/she is.) ___ ___

Are you prideful? (A prideful person
finds it very difficult to admit mistakes
and to ask for forgiveness.) ___ ___

Are you rude? ___ ___

Do you look out for your own interests rather
than putting others first? ___ ___

Do you become angered easily? ___ ___

Do you keep a record of it when someone does
you wrong? ___ ___

Are you ever happy with evil? ___ ___

Are you full of joy when truth is spoken? ___ ___

Do you protect God and those you love? ___ ___

Do you trust in God? ___ ___

Do you put your hope in God? ___ ___

Do you ever give up on God? ___ ___

Do you fail to be there for those you love? ___ ___

The exercise you just completed may have been a real eye-opener for you. Perhaps you discovered that you do not love God and others according to God's definition of love. If that is the case, take a moment to pray and ask God to forgive you. Make a decision today to love according to God's definition. Ask God to help you. Faithfully, He will answer your prayer as long as you cooperate with His Spirit through obedience. He will teach you how to love. We'll look more closely at the qualities of love later in this study.

Before closing today, let's look at one more verse that sheds light on how you can demonstrate your love for God. Turning in your Bible to John 14:15 (NT), read this verse. Keep in mind that this is Jesus speaking. Answer the question below.

6. According to Jesus, what must you do to prove that you love Him?

_____

Jesus said, **"If you love me, you will obey what I command."** Your obedience to God proves that you love Him. When you obey God, you are putting Him first. When you disobey Him, you are putting yourself before God. At that moment of disobedience, you are choosing not to love God.

Praise God because He is faithful to forgive us of our sins when we confess and turn from them! Do you need to confess to God that there have been times in the past when you did not put Him first? Take a moment to pray to Him and confess those times. Again, ask Him to forgive you and to help you as you make the commitment to love Him and obey His commands. Remember, you must choose daily to love God by obeying His Word and His Spirit as He guides you through your life. This is a very important step to developing and maintaining a relationship with Him.

In Lessons 6, 7, and 8, we still study more closely about loving God through obedience. See you there!

That's enough for today. Let's review what you've learned:

- Jesus said that the two most important commands in the Bible are: loving God with all your heart, soul and mind and loving others as you love yourself.
- In 1 Corinthians 13:4-8a, God defines love.
- Love is patient, kind, and it does not envy.
- Love does not boast, is not proud, rude or self-seeking.
- Love is not easily angered and keeps no record of wrongs.
- Love does not delight in evil but rejoices with the truth.
- Love always protects, trusts, hopes and perseveres.
- Love never fails.
- Loving God means obeying His commands.

This week's memory verse is Jeremiah 7:23 (OT). It is written below. Say it to yourself three times.

"But I gave them this command: Obey me, and I will be your God and you will be my people. Walk in all the ways I command you, that it may go well with you."

7. Write this week's memory verse in the space provided below.

_____

_____

_____

_____

Lesson 6

Becoming God's Friend

Throughout the Old Testament, God entered into covenants with men whom He could trust. A covenant is an agreement. In each covenant that God entered into, He agreed to provide, protect and bless the individual man and his family in return for his obedience and love toward God. What kind of man is worthy of God's trust? In today's lesson, you'll learn what it takes to become a friend of God.

You have already studied a bit about Adam. Entering into a covenant with Adam, God promised to provide, protect and bless him in return for his obedience and love. Unfortunately, Adam broke that covenant when he disobeyed God.

Another Old Testament individual with whom God entered into a covenant was Noah. What kind of man was he? To find out, turn to and read Genesis 6:9 (OT). Answer the question below by writing your answer in the space provided.

1.   According to Genesis 6:9, what kind of man was Noah?

_____

_____

Noah was a righteous man, blameless among his people. He walked with God. Although Noah did not have the Bible to read, he must have spent time with God in prayer, praise and worship. Undoubtedly, he loved and obeyed God. In return for his love and obedience, God entered into a covenant with Noah. God spared Noah's life along with the lives of his family members in the great flood. Everyone else on earth perished.

The next man God entered into a covenant with was Abram. God came to Abram and made him an offer. God promised to give Abram his own land, children, protection, provision and enormous blessings in return for Abram's love and obedience. In other words, God made Abram an offer he couldn't refuse. God even changed his name to Abraham, which means the father of many. But why did God choose Abram? To find out, turn to Hebrews 11:8-12 (NT). Read this passage, and answer the question below by placing a check mark beside the correct answer.

2. According to this passage, what did Abraham do by faith? (Check all answers that are correct.)

    ____ a. He obeyed God and went to a land about which he did not know.

    ____ b. He made his home in the Promised Land where he was a stranger.

    ____ c. He considered God faithful to keep His promises.

    ____ d. He became a father in his old age.

Abraham obeyed God. Considering God faithful to keep the promises He had made, Abraham trusted God although many of those promises were impossible in the natural. In return for his obedience, God entered into a covenant with Abraham. Abraham had a son named Isaac. Isaac had a son named Jacob, and Jacob's twelve sons became the heads of the twelve tribes of Israel.

God also entered into a covenant with a man named David. What kind of man was he? To find out, turn to and read Acts 13:22 (NT). Answer the question below by putting a check mark beside the correct answer. The "He" in this verse is God.

3. According to God, what kind of man was David? (Check all answers that are correct.)

    ____ a. Jesse's favorite son

    ____ b. a man after God's own heart

    ____ c. obedient to all God called him to do

David was a man after God's own heart. He did everything God commanded him to do because of his love and obedience toward God. As a result, David was made king over Israel. Victoriously, God led David and his army in times of war. He provided, protected and blessed David in every way. Additionally, God promised David that He would establish an eternal kingdom through his family line.

After David's death, God extended His covenant to David's son, Solomon. Initially, Solomon loved and obeyed God. In time, however, he turned away from God and began to worship idols. Because of this, God lifted His protection, provision and blessings from Solomon's family, and the nation of Israel was eventually divided.

For the sake of David, and because God loves His people, He renewed His covenant with the people of Israel. Sadly though, they would not continue to walk in His ways. They would not continue to love and obey God. Eventually, Israel was conquered and forced to leave the land God had given them through Abraham.

But what about God's promise to David to establish an eternal kingdom through David's family line? Fulfilling His promise, God sent Jesus Christ to earth. From the tribe of Judah, Jesus was a member of David's family line. He lived on earth 33 years. At 30, He began His ministry of love and salvation. At 33, He was crucified for the sins of all mankind. Returning to earth one day, Jesus will succeed in establishing His earthly kingdom. It will be an everlasting one, fulfilling the promise God made to David.

Through Christ, God offers a new and better covenant to all people who confess and believe Jesus as Lord. Through your faith, love and obedience to Him, you can enter into a covenant with God. As you begin to spend time with Him in His Word, through prayer, and in praise and worship, you will begin to be transformed into the image of Jesus. You will become God's friend. Psalm 15 describes the characteristics of a man or woman who loves and obeys God. Turning to this psalm, read it. Fill in the blanks below.

4.   According to Psalm 15:1-5, who dwells in God's sanctuary (presence) and lives on His holy hill?

"He whose walk is _____ **and who does what is**

_____ **, who speaks the** _____ **from his**

heart and has no _____ **on his tongue, who does**

his neighbor no _____ **and casts no**_____

on his fellowman, who _____ **a vile man but**

24

_____ those who fear the Lord, who _____

his oath even when it hurts, who _____ his money

without usury and does not accept a _____ against the

innocent. He who does these things will never be _____.”

Searching for someone He can trust, God is looking for those who will love and obey Him. Does that description fit you? Are you "friend material" where God is concerned? If not, you can be. In Lesson 7, you'll learn how. See you there!

That's enough for today. Let's review what you've learned:

- God entered into covenants with Adam, Noah, Abraham and his descendants.
- God also entered into a covenant with David to establish an eternal kingdom through his family line.
- Jesus fulfilled the covenant promise God made to David.
- Through faith in Jesus, you can enter into a covenant with God.
- Psalm 15 describes a covenant keeper.

This week's memory verse is Jeremiah 7:23 (OT). It is written below. Say it to yourself three times.

"But I gave them this command: Obey me, and I will be your God and you will be my people. Walk in all the ways I command you, that it may go well with you."

5.   Write this week's memory verse in the space provided below.

_____

_____

_____

_____

Lesson 7

Obeying God

Over the past few weeks, you have learned that in order to develop and strengthen your relationship with God you must spend time with Him, love and obey Him. You are immensely blessed to have God's commandments so accessible to you through His Word, the Bible. By reading and studying God's Word, you can learn exactly what He expects from you.

In the Old Testament times, people did not have the Bible. God communicated His commandments to the people through His prophets. Utilizing a man named Moses, God conveyed His commandments to the nation of Israel. The first of these are known as the Ten Commandments. Turning in your Bible to Exodus 20:1-17 (OT), read these verses from the passage titled, "The Ten Commandments." Using the word list below, complete the following sentences taken from the passage you just read.

Word List

false	adultery	Honor	bow	murder	name
	covet	steal	gods	holy	idol

1.   God said, "You shall have no other _____ before me."

2.   "You shall not make for yourself an _____ in the form of anything in heaven above or on the earth beneath or in the

waters below. You shall not _____ down to them or worship them;…."

3.   "You shall not misuse the _____ of the Lord your God…."

4.   "Remember the Sabbath day by keeping it _____."

5. "_____ your father and your mother, so that you may live long in the land the Lord your God is giving you."

6. "You shall not _____."

7. "You shall not commit _____."

8. "You shall not _____."

9. "You shall not give _____ testimony against your neighbor."

10. "You shall not _____ your neighbor's house … or anything that belongs to your neighbor."

Did you notice that the first four commandments deal with man's relationship with God while the last six deal with man's relationship with each other? Fairly straightforward and easy to comprehend, these commandments were communicated to the nation of Israel thousands of years ago. But are they still pertinent in the day in which we live? In other words, are you still expected to obey these laws under the new covenant? Jesus addressed this very issue in the Beatitudes. Turning in your Bible to Matthew 5:17-20 (NT), read this passage titled, "The Fulfillment of the Law." Using the word list provided, complete the following sentences.

Word List

| disappear | abolish | great | least |

11. Jesus did not come to _____ the Law or the Prophets.

12. Jesus said that the Law will remain the same until heaven and earth

_____ .

13. Anyone who breaks the laws of God and teaches others to break them, too, will be called the _____ in the kingdom of heaven.

14. But those who practice God's laws and teach them to others will be called _____ in the kingdom of heaven.

According to Jesus, you are still expected to obey the Ten Commandments. In fact, Jesus further explained the commandments, adding to them in Matthew 5:21 through 7:29 (NT). Specifically, He addressed murder, adultery, divorce, taking oaths, revenge and loving your enemies. Additionally, He spoke about giving to the needy, prayer and fasting and the issue of money. Jesus also taught on the subjects of worrying, judging others, seeking God, false prophets, and being grounded in the Lord.

In Matthew 7:12 (NT), Jesus revealed the key to developing and maintaining good relationships with others. Turning to this verse, read it.

15. Write Matthew 7:12 in the space provided below.

_____

_____

_____

Did you know that the Golden Rule originated with Jesus? Do unto others as you would have them do unto you. In doing so, you will be obeying God.

Did Jesus have anything to say about developing and maintaining a relationship with God? Yes, He did. To find out what He said, turn to and read John 14:21 (NT).

16. Write John 14:21 in the space that follows.

_____

_____

_____

_____

Obedience is the key to developing and maintaining a relationship with God. The more you obey Him, the more He reveals Himself to you, and the stronger your relationship becomes. Are you willing to obey God? If you are, He will bless you in every area of your life. That doesn't mean you'll be exempt from trials or tests. Jesus said, **"In this world you will have trouble."** But the good news is He didn't stop there. He added, **"But take heart! I have overcome the world"** (John 16:33b). That's good news! If God is on your side, who can be against you? (Romans 8:31 NT).

Will you obey God in every area of your life? Are you willing to put your money where your mouth is? Lesson 8 will teach you the importance of obeying God in the area of tithing. See you there!

That's enough for today. Let's review what you've learned:

- Jesus came to fulfill, not abolish, God's Old Testament Laws.
- Jesus' advice for building relationships with people is following the Golden Rule.
- Jesus' advice for building a relationship with God is obedience.

This week's memory verse is Jeremiah 7:23 (OT). It is written below. Say it to yourself three times.

"But I gave them this command: Obey me, and I will be your God and you will be my people. Walk in all the ways I command you, that it may go well with you."

17. Write this week's memory verse in the space provided below.

_____

_____

_____

_____

Lesson 8

Putting Your Money Where Your Mouth Is

In Lesson 7, you studied about the Ten Commandments. In addition to these commands, God has given His people other commandments that He expects them to obey. One of these commandments is to tithe a minimum of 10 percent of your earnings back to Him. Included in the Bible are numerous scriptures regarding the importance of tithing. In this lesson, we will examine several of them.

Early in the Bible in Genesis 14:20 (OT), the subject of tithing is addressed. Upon entering into a covenant with Abram, God changed his name to Abraham, which means "the father of many." Promising to bless, provide and protect Abraham and his descendants, God demanded their love and obedience toward Him in return.

When God first came to Abram, He told him to leave his country and his people and go to a new land that He would show him. Without hesitation, Abram obeyed God and began his journey. Abram's nephew, Lot, accompanied Abram and his wife, Sarai. For some time, they journeyed to new places. During this time, God blessed Abram with livestock, silver, gold and people. Lot was blessed, too. However, because the land was not sufficient for both Abram and Lot's livestock, they decided to part ways. Lot settled in a town called Sodom while Abram settled in the land of Canaan.

Populated by evil people, Sodom was a wicked place. It wasn't long before Lot found himself in trouble. War broke out in Sodom, and Lot was captured and taken prisoner. Abram found out about it. He decided to round up some of his men and go after Lot. Pick up with the story in Genesis 14:14-20 (OT). Read these verses from the passage titled, "Abram Rescues Lot." Answer the following questions by writing your answers in the spaces provided.

1.   In pursuit of Lot, how many men did Abram take with him? _____

2. Was Abram successful in retrieving Lot? _____

3. What else did Abram recover?_____

_____

4. Who came out to meet Abram when he returned from defeating those who had taken Lot?

_____

_____

5. Who was Melchizedek? _____

6. What did Abram give the king of Salem?_____

With God's help, Abram was able to rescue Lot and bring him back safely. Additionally, Abram recovered all the goods, possessions and people who had been captured by the enemies. The king of Sodom and the king of Salem came out to greet Abram upon his return. The king of Salem was a priest of God, and He blessed Abram. His name was Melchizedek. Recognizing Him, Abram gave Him a tenth of everything he had. Who was this priest of Salem? To find out, turn over to Hebrews 7:1-3 (NT). Read these verses from the passage titled, "Melchizedek the Priest." Answer the questions that follow.

7. What does Melchizedek's name mean? _____

_____

8. What was unusual about Melchizedek's ancestors?_____

_____

9. What else was unusual about him?_____

_____

10. To whom is Melchizedek compared? _____

The priest, Melchizedek, came out of nowhere with no parents or family. Hebrews 7:3 states that He was without beginning or end of days, like the Son of God. Abram tithed to Melchizedek, who was obviously God's representative. Could Melchizedek, the king of peace, be Jesus? Certainly, it is possible that He was!

STOP FOR TODAY. FINISH LESSON NEXT TIME.

From the beginning, God addressed the subject of tithing. Faithfully, Abram tithed. In return, God blessed him. There are many other passages in the Bible that relate to tithing. One of them is found in Malachi 3:6-18 (OT). Read this passage titled, "Robbing God." Below are several statements related to this passage. Put a "T" in front of those statements that are true. Put an "F" in front of those statements that are false.

____ **11.** God was upset with Israel (the descendants of Jacob) because they had turned away from Him, disobeying His commands.

____ **12.** Continually, Israel had tithed.

____ **13.** God said that Israel had robbed Him.

____ **14.** God commanded Israel to bring His tithes into the storehouse (temple), and He would pour out more blessings than they could contain.

____ **15.** The people of Israel had also spoken harsh words against God.

____ **16.** God does show favor toward those who obey Him and tithe.

Did you know that when you do not give God at least 10 percent of your earnings, you are robbing Him? On the other hand, when you are faithful to tithe, God pours out more blessings on you than you have room enough to contain! That's exciting! Why would anyone refuse to give God His rightful tithe? Probably, the greatest reason is the love of money. Greed and fear are other reasons why people don't tithe. They're afraid that if they give away some of their money, they won't have enough to take care of their own needs. God's Word promises that if we seek Him first, He'll take care of all of our needs (Matthew 6:33 NT).

When Jesus walked upon the earth, He taught about the importance of giving to God. One of His teachings is found in Matthew 19:16-30 (NT). Turning to this passage titled, "The Rich Young Man," read it. Below are several statements related to this passage. Put a "T" in front of those statements that are true. Put an "F" in front of those statements that are false.

_____ **17.** The rich young man asked Jesus how he could get eternal life.

_____ **18.** Jesus began reciting some of the Ten commandments to the rich man.

_____ **19.** When Jesus told the rich young man that he must sell all he had and follow Him, the rich ruler obeyed.

_____ **20.** Jesus said that it is difficult for a rich man to enter heaven.

_____ **21.** With God all things are possible.

_____ **22.** Jesus told His disciples that everyone who makes sacrifices on earth in order to follow Him will one day be rewarded.

Giving up his material wealth and possessions in order to follow Jesus was more than the rich young man could bear. Sadly, what he gave up that day was far more valuable. He could have walked with Christ, learned from Him and blessed others with the love of God. He could have earned for himself an eternal reward that far exceeded anything he had acquired on earth. Greed and fear kept him from taking what God so freely offered to him that day because he loved money more than God. According to the Bible, the love of money is the root of all evil (1 Timothy 6:10 NT). Don't make the same mistake as did the rich young man. Wisely, make a decision today to obey God and tithe at least 10 percent of your income to Him. He will bless you for it, and you will have the peace of knowing you are right with God!

That's enough for today. Let's review what you've learned:

- After rescuing his nephew Lot, the stolen goods, possessions and the people captured by the enemy, Abram tithed to Melchizedek.
- Melchizedek was the king of Salem, which means the king of peace, and He was a priest of God.
- Melchizedek was, more than likely, Jesus Christ.
- God became upset with the people of Israel because they were not tithing to Him.
- God promises favor and blessings to those who tithe faithfully.
- Jesus told the rich young man that if he wanted to be perfect, he should sell all of his possessions and follow Him.
- The rich young man refused to sell his things and follow Jesus.
- Jesus said that all who follow Him would one day be rewarded.

This week's memory verse is Jeremiah 7:23 (OT). It is written below. Say it to yourself three times.

"But I gave them this command: Obey me, and I will be your God and you will be my people. Walk in all the ways I command you, that it may go well with you."

23. Write this week's memory verse in the space provided below.

_____

_____

_____

_____

It's time to take Test 2.

Lesson 9

Relationship with Parents

In Lesson 7, you studied about the Ten Commandments. The fourth commandment is: **"Honor your father and your mother, so that you may live long in the land the Lord your God is giving you."** In addition to other commands, God gave this commandment to the Israelites as they were journeying toward the Promised Land. To honor someone means to love, respect and obey that person.

The commandment to honor your father and mother is found several times in the Bible. When God repeats something, it is extremely important. Below are several verses instructing children to love, respect and obey their parents. Look up each verse, and read it. Match the verse's address on the left to its content on the right by writing the letter in the blank provided.

	Verse's address		**Verse's content**
___ 1.	Leviticus 19:3a (OT)	**a.**	Listen to your father's instruction, and do not forsake your mother's teaching.
___ 2.	Proverbs 1:8 (OT)	**b.**	Honor and obey your parents in the Lord, for this is right.
___ 3.	Ephesians 6:1-2 (NT)	**c.**	Obey your parents in everything, for this pleases the Lord.
___ 4.	Colossians 3:20 (NT)	**d.**	You must respect your mother and father.

In Lesson 7, you learned that Jesus did not come to abolish God's Old Testament commandments but rather to fulfill them. Demonstrating that man is responsible for loving and obeying God, Jesus' life reflected the utmost devotion to God. Loving, respecting and obeying His parents was one manner in which Jesus demonstrated His allegiance to the Father. The first time this was evident was when Jesus was twelve years old. He had gone with his parents to the Passover Feast in Jerusalem. After the Feast had concluded, Jesus' parents began the journey home. Traveling with a large group of people, Jesus' parents assumed that He was somewhere among the group. After they had traveled a day, they realized that Jesus was not with them. Returning to Jerusalem, they discovered Him at the temple. Jesus' mother scolded Him for staying behind. Jesus was surprised that His parents did not know He could be found at the temple—in His Father's house. Then what happened? To find out, turn in your Bible to Luke 2:51-52 (NT). Read these verses, and answer the questions below by writing your answer in the spaces provided.

5. Jesus returned with his parents to Nazareth and was _____ to them.

6. **"And Jesus grew in wisdom and stature, and in favor with**

_____ and men."

Certainly, Jesus would have grown in wisdom, stature and in favor with God if He was obeying His parents, and, indeed, He was. Luke 2:51 (NT) confirms it.

Another example of Jesus' obedience toward His mother is recorded in John 2:1-11 (NT). Turning to this passage titled "Jesus Changes Water to Wine," read it. Below are several statements related to the passage you just read. If the statement is true, put a "T" in front of it. If it is false, put an "F" in front of it.

____ **7.** Jesus, His mother and His disciples were invited to a wedding.

____ **8.** When they ran out of wine, Jesus' disciples came to Him for help.

___ **9.** Jesus told His mother that His time had not yet come.

___ **10.** Jesus' mother told the servants to obey Jesus.

___ **11.** Jesus refused to do anything about the wine situation.

___ **12.** Jesus told the servants to fill the jars with water.

___ **13.** When the master of the banquet tasted the water, it was sour wine.

___ **14.** Jesus performed His first miracle by turning water into the finest wine!

Because the wine had not yet fermented, there was no alcohol content in it. The Word is clear that drinking alcohol is dangerous and is not a good idea.

Did you notice that when Jesus' mother approached Him about the situation, He told her that His time had not yet come? In other words, it was not time for Him to begin His public ministry. Jesus knew that performing miracles would get everyone's attention and launch His ministry. Rather than disobey and disappoint His mother, however, Jesus did what she asked Him to do. He turned the water into wine and not just any wine. It was some of the best wine that the master of the banquet had ever tasted. Who would expect any less from Jesus?

As a child, Jesus obeyed His parents. As a man, He obeyed His mother at the wedding in Cana. Perhaps the most loving and respectful act that Jesus demonstrated in regards to His mother, however, occurred during His crucifixion. After being beaten, tortured and mocked, Jesus was hanging on the cross, suffering terribly. His Father God turned His face away from Jesus because He is so holy, He cannot look upon sin. Jesus took upon Himself the sins of the world while hanging there. Looking down, Jesus saw His mother standing at the foot of the cross. Who would care for her after His death? He had to know that someone would be there for her. Turning in your Bible to John 19:26-27 (NT), read these verses. Answer the question that follows.

15. What did Jesus say to His mother and His beloved disciple, John?

_____

_____

In spite of the fact that He was suffering and in terrible pain, Jesus took the time to tell John to care for His mother as if she were his own. Loving her with His entire being, Jesus set an example for all children to follow.

Respect, obey and love your mother and your father. Care for them in their older years. Richly, God will bless you for it. First Timothy 5:4 (NT) is a confirmation of this. In closing, read it. **"But if a widow has children or grandchildren, these should learn first of all to put their religion into practice by caring for their own family and so repaying their parents and grandparents, for this is pleasing to God."**

That's enough for today. Let's review what you've learned:

- God's Word commands children to obey and care for their parents.
- Jesus obeyed His parents when He was a child as well as when He was a grown man.
- At the cross, Jesus made certain that John would care for His mother after His death.

This week's memory verse is 1 John 3:15 (NT). It is written below. Say it to yourself three times.

"Anyone who hates his brother is a murderer, and you know that no murderer has eternal life in him."

16. Write this week's memory verse in the space provided.

_____

_____

_____

Lesson 10

Sibling Relationships

Throughout the Bible, there are countless stories of sibling relationships filled with hatred, jealousy and even murder. What is at the core of this strife? Jealousy is the culprit. In today's lesson, you will take a look at some of the sibling relationships in the Bible and discover what went wrong and why. Additionally, you will see just how destructive jealousy can be among siblings.

To begin, you must go back in time to the first siblings on earth. Visit Cain and Abel, the sons of Adam and Eve. Turning in your Bible to Genesis 4:1-16 (OT), read this passage titled, "Cain and Abel." Below are several statements taken from this story. Put a "T" in front of those statements that are true. Put an "F" in front of those statements that are false.

____   **1.**   Abel was a shepherd, while Cain worked the ground.

____   **2.**   Abel offered to God the fattest parts of some of the firstborn lambs from his flock, and Cain offered some of the fruits he had grown.

____   **3.**   God was pleased with both Abel and Cain's offerings.

____   **4.**   Cain became angry with Abel because God was pleased with Abel's offering, but He was not pleased with Cain's.

____   **5.**   God told Cain that sin desired to have him, but he should master it.

____   **6.**   Abel killed Cain.

____   **7.**   God punished Cain by putting a curse on him.

____   **8.**   Part of Cain's punishment was that no matter how diligently he worked the ground, it would produce no crops for him.

Why was Cain so angry with his brother, Abel? He was jealous of Abel because God accepted Abel's offering, but He did not accept Cain's offering. Visiting Cain, God warned him not to allow sin to consume him. Sadly, Cain ignored God's warning and killed his brother, Abel.

To punish Cain, God banned him from His presence and put a curse on him. Although Cain labored diligently to grow things, the ground would not produce crops for him. Because Cain loved to garden, this was probably the worst punishment God could have given him. Cain lost a lot more that day than the ability to garden. He lost his brother, and the blood of Abel would forever be upon Cain's shoulders.

This is just one account of the damage that jealousy and strife can cause among siblings. As you read the Bible, you come across many stories similar to that of Cain and Abel. Joseph was Jacob's eleventh son. God changed Jacob's name to Israel, and his descendants became known as the nation of Israel. Jacob favored Joseph over his older brothers. Favoring one child over another is wrong. Even if that is the case, however, no one has the right to take revenge into his or her own hands. That is exactly what Joseph's older brothers did. They threw Joseph into a pit. Instead of leaving him there to die, the brothers opted to sell Joseph to slave traders who happened to be in the area. Deceiving their father, the brothers told Jacob that a wild animal had killed Joseph. Jacob was heartbroken while Joseph was taken to Egypt.

Joseph possessed favor with God and man. Years passed, and he rose to a position of great authority in Egypt. A famine struck the land, but before it hit, Joseph came up with an idea to store enough grain to feed the people during the famine. The famine reached Jacob and his family. Traveling to Egypt, Joseph's brothers went to purchase grain so that they would not starve to death. When Joseph saw his brothers, he recognized them, but they did not recognize him. In the end, Joseph revealed his identity to his brothers, and the family was reunited. Joseph had no ill feelings toward his brothers for what they had done to him. He loved them, and he forgave them. Jacob and his entire family moved to Egypt to be near Joseph.

Over time, Jacob's descendants grew in number. Joseph died as did his memory. Fearing that the people of Israel might rebel and make war against them, the Egyptians forced the people of Israel into slavery. For many years, Jacob's descendants were mistreated and abused. Finally, God sent Moses to lead the people of Israel out of Egypt toward the Promised Land! One cannot help but wonder if Jacob's family would have been spared years of pain and suffering if only Joseph's brothers had loved him rather than hated him.

STOP FOR TODAY. FINISH LESSON NEXT TIME.

Moses, too, had siblings, a brother named Aaron and a sister named Miriam. They became jealous of Moses because God chose him to lead the people of Israel out of Egypt and into the Promised Land. Aaron and Miriam blamed their anger on the fact that Moses had married a woman of whom they did not approve. Take a look at their story, and see what happened to them. Turning in your Bible to Numbers 12:1-15 (OT), read this passage titled, "Miriam and Aaron Oppose Moses." Below are several statements. Put a "T" in front of those statements that are true. Put an "F" in front of those statements that are false.

9. Miriam and Aaron began to speak out against Moses.

10. Miriam and Aaron said that God did not speak only through Moses but also through them.

11. Moses was full of pride.

12. God called Miriam, Aaron and Moses out to the Tent of Meeting.

13. God spoke highly of Moses, but He confronted Miriam and Aaron for speaking against Moses.

14. Neither Miriam nor Aaron were punished for speaking out against their brother.

15. Moses was so upset with his siblings that he did not care that Miriam had been struck with leprosy.

God does not reveal why Miriam was struck with leprosy, and Aaron was not. Certainly, God was very upset with both of them for trash talking their brother. Notice Moses' reaction to the situation. Crying out to God, Moses petitioned Him to heal Miriam. There was no bitterness in his heart toward her or Aaron for what they had spoken against him. Like Joseph, Moses loved his siblings regardless of what they had done to him. He chose to forgive them. Answering Moses' plea, God healed Miriam after seven days.

Sibling relationships are so important. There is an old saying, "Blood is thicker than water." Faithful family members will be there for you when everyone else deserts you. Siblings are a gift from God. God expects you to love one another. When you choose to argue and fight with your brother or sister, you disobey God. That is a sin. James 3:16 (NT) says, **"For where you have envy and selfish ambition, there you find disorder and every evil practice."** Don't open the door to disorder and evil practices. Make a decision today to love your brothers and/or sisters. God will bless you for it!

That's enough for today. Let's review what you've learned.

- Cain killed Abel because he was jealous of him.
- Joseph's brothers sold him into slavery because they were jealous of him.
- Miriam and Aaron were jealous of their brother, Moses, and spoke out against him.
- Envy and strife between siblings are sins.
- Sin opens the door to disorder and every evil practice.

This week's memory verse is 1 John 3:15 (NT). It is written below. Say it to yourself three times.

"Anyone who hates his brother is a murderer, and you know that no murderer has eternal life in him."

16. Write this week's memory verse in the space provided.

_____

_____

_____

Lesson 11

Relationships with Authority Figures

It is extremely important to God that you obey those who have authority over you. Ben Franklin once said, "He who cannot obey cannot command." If you cannot submit to authority, you have no business having authority over anyone else.

Honestly, pride is one reason people rebel against authority. Pride is not a godly quality. The opposite of pride is humility. You'll remember from Lesson 10 that Moses was a humble man, and God exalted him. Humbly, Moses placed the needs of others before his own. Humility is a godly quality and one that you must possess in order to obey those in authority over you.

Before we proceed, one issue must be clarified. If someone who has authority over you is hurting you in any way, that is not okay. Authority does not give anyone the right to abuse you. If an authority figure in your life is verbally or physically abusive to you, tell someone you can trust about it. It's not your fault, and it needs to stop!

Turning in your Bible to Hebrews 13:17 (NT), read this verse. Answer the questions below by writing your answers in the spaces provided.

1. According to Hebrews 13:17, whom should you obey?

    _____

2. Who are some of the leaders in your life? (Example: teacher, coach.)

    _____

    _____

God's Word is clear. You are to obey the leaders in your life. Being responsible for you, your leaders must give an account to God if they fail to demonstrate godly leadership. On the other hand, if you are disobedient to the leaders in your life, you will have to answer to God for that. You are to be a blessing rather than a burden to those who have authority over you.

God is a God of order. He orchestrates levels of authority to rule over the earth. Even when it seems He is not in control, God is. If you don't believe it, turn to Proverbs 21:1 (NT). Read this verse, and answer the question below.

3.   Who, according to this verse, is in control of a king's heart? _____

God is sovereign. He is in complete control, and He can direct the words and actions of anyone He so chooses, even if that person is a king or a president. Certainly, it is important for a democracy such as we enjoy in the United States to vote for godly leaders. History has proven that when a godly leader is in charge, circumstances and events are more likely to go according to God's plan. Regardless of who is in charge, however, God can and does direct his/her steps if someone somewhere is praying God's Word over him/her.

Looking at one more passage in the Bible that instructs Christians to obey those who have authority over them, turn to and read Romans 13:1-7 (NT). This passage is titled, "Submission to the Authorities." Below are several incomplete statements. Using the word list provided, complete each one.

Word List

Respect	taxes	rebel	servants
authorities	conscience		punishment

4.   God establishes the _____ upon the earth.

5.   When you _____ against someone who has authority over you, you are rebelling against God as well as the authority figure.

6.   When you to submit (obey) authorities in your life, you don't need to

fear their _____.

7. Authorities are God's _____ and are meant to do you good.

8. Fear of punishment and a guilty _____ are reasons to obey authorities.

9. Paying _____ is a requirement rather than an option.

10. _____ and honor should also be paid to authorities.

According to this passage, God establishes authorities in the earth. Authorities are God's servants. Those who rebel against God's authorities are rebelling against God Himself. Although you may not always agree with their leadership, you do not have the right to break the laws established by those in authority. Remember, though, just because someone has authority over you does not give that person the right to abuse you in any way. Again, if an authority figure in your life is abusing you, tell an adult whom you can trust about it. Otherwise, obey the authorities in your life. Honor and respect them because God commands it of you.

That's enough for today. Let's review what you've learned:

- You should obey the leaders in your life.
- God establishes authorities on the earth.
- Your leaders must give an account to God.
- When you rebel against authority, you are rebelling against God.

This week's memory verse is 1 John 3:15 (NT). It is written below. Say it to yourself three times.

"Anyone who hates his brother is a murderer, and you know that no murderer has eternal life in him."

11. Write this week's memory verse in the space provided.

_____

_____

_____

Lesson 12

Choosing Godly Friends

Certainly, friendships are a very important part of our lives. Throughout the Bible, there are several stories of friends helping one another. Jonathan and David were best friends. Warning David that Jonathan's father, King Saul, was planning to kill him, Jonathan saved David's life a time or two. On the other hand, Job's friends weren't really very good friends to Job at all. Criticizing Job, his friends offered him terrible advice. Choosing the right kind of friends is very important.

What does God's Word have to say about friendships? How do you choose a friend, and what qualities do you look for in a friend? What kind of friend are you to be to others? Today's lesson, as well as Lesson 13, will address these very important questions. You may be surprised to discover the answers. To begin, turn in your Bible to Proverbs 12:26 (OT). Read this verse, and answer the question below by placing a check mark beside the correct answer.

1.   According to this verse, what is a righteous man?

　　____　a.　cautious in friendship
　　____　b.　led astray
　　____　c.　wicked

A righteous man is cautious in friendship. What does that mean? It means that he doesn't enter into friendships carelessly. A godly or righteous man enters into friendships carefully and with much thought. Why? What's the danger of becoming friends with anyone and everyone? Befriending someone who does not love and obey God is a dangerous act. When you hang around ungodly people, their ungodliness rubs off on you. Ungodliness is contagious. If you don't believe it, turn to 1 Corinthians 15:33 (NT). Read this verse, and answer the following question.

2. According to 1 Corinthians 15:33, what does bad company do?

   ____   a.   It misleads people.
   ____   b.   It builds character.
   ____   c.   It corrupts good character.

According to this verse, bad company corrupts good character. Does that mean you should ignore people who are not seeking after and obeying God? Should you be rude and mean to them? No. You should demonstrate God's love to them through kindness. You should care about them, and, most importantly, pray for them. BUT you should not select these people to be your closest friends nor should you run around with them because they could pull you away from God.

When God was giving instructions to Israel concerning the Promised Land, He commanded the Israelites to destroy all the inhabitants. The people who lived in the land were evil. Worshipping false gods, they even sacrificed their children to these gods! God knew that if the people of Israel lived among them, they would turn the hearts of the Israelites against God. Turning in your Bible to Deuteronomy 7, read this chapter titled, "Driving Out the Nations." Answer the questions that follow by placing a check mark beside the correct answer.

3. How was it possible for the people of Israel to destroy seven nations stronger than they were?

   ____   a.   because they were great warriors
   ____   b.   because God would deliver the enemies into their hands
   ____   c.   because the nations feared Israel

4. What did God command Israel to do to the inhabitants of the land? (Check all answers that are correct.)

   ____   a.   destroy them totally
   ____   b.   make no treaty with them
   ____   c.   show them no mercy
   ____   d.   do not intermarry with them

5. What did God say would happen if Israel did not destroy the inhabitants of the land? (Check all answers that are correct.)

    ____   a.   they would turn their hearts away from following God
    ____   b.   they would cause Israel to follow their gods
    ____   c.   God's anger would burn against Israel

6. What else did God instruct Israel to do regarding the inhabitants of the land? (Check all that are correct.)

    ____   a.   break down their altars
    ____   b.   smash their sacred stones
    ____   c.   cut down their Asherah poles
    ____   d.   burn their idols in fire

7. Why did God choose Israel to be His people?

    ____   a.   because they were numerous
    ____   b.   because they were unholy
    ____   c.   because He loved them and wanted to keep the oath He had sworn to their forefathers

8. To whom does God keep His covenant of love?

    ____   a.   to those who love Him and keep His commands
    ____   b.   to Pharaoh
    ____   c.   to all generations

9. What did God promise to those who follow His decrees? (Check all that are correct.)

    ____   a.   to love and bless them
    ____   b.   to increase their numbers
    ____   c.   to bless the fruit of their womb (their children)
    ____   d.   to bless the crops of their land and their animals

10. What else did God promise to those who follow His decrees? (Check all that are correct.)

    ____   a.   children
    ____   b.   freedom from sickness and disease
    ____   c.   pity

11. Why did God tell Israel not to pity the inhabitants of the land?

    ____   a.   because they were stronger than Israel
    ____   b.   because Israel would be a snare to them
    ____   c.   because they would be a snare to Israel

12. Why should Israel not fear the inhabitants of the land?

    ____   a.   because the inhabitants were not warriors
    ____   b.   because God had delivered Israel from Egypt and would do the same for them against the inhabitants
    ____   c.   because Israel was larger and stronger than the inhabitants of the land

13. What did God say about Israel?

    ____   a.   that they would be confused
    ____   b.   that no one would be able to stand against them
    ____   c.   that they would be destroyed

14. Why did God instruct Israel not to take the silver and gold from the gods and images that belonged to the inhabitants of the land?

    ____   a.   because it's wrong to steal
    ____   b.   because it wasn't real silver and gold
    ____   c.   because it would ensnare (or trap) Israel

That's a powerful chapter. You might be thinking to yourself, *Taking land from people is one thing, but destroying them is serious.* Think again. These people were evil. They worshipped false gods. They were not nice folks. Israel was God's chosen people. Entering into a covenant with Abraham many years prior to this time, God promised to bless, protect and provide for Abraham and his descendants in return for their obedience.

Abraham had a son named Isaac. Isaac had a son named Jacob. Jacob had twelve sons. These twelve sons became the twelve tribes that comprised the nation of Israel. You'll remember from Lesson 10 that Joseph was one of Jacob's sons. After his brothers sold Joseph into slavery, he wound up in Egypt. Joseph rose to a powerful position in Egypt. In time, Jacob's entire family moved there. Some time after Joseph's death, his family became slaves to the Egyptians. They cried out to God, and He remembered His covenant with Abraham. Miraculously, God led Israel out of Egypt. He promised to restore to them their land, but they had to destroy its inhabitants. If they did not, God said the people of the land would turn Israel's hearts away from Him.

Sadly, Israel did not obey God completely. They did not destroy all the inhabitants of the land. Guess what happened? As God had said, the inhabitants who remained in that land turned the hearts of the Israelites against God. They began worshipping their gods. For a time, God turned His face away from Israel. The nation became divided into two kingdoms. Eventually, both kingdoms were conquered and driven out of their God-given land.

God is not asking you to destroy ungodly people around you. However, you must realize that when you place yourself in an ungodly environment, over time, your heart may be turned away from God. You saw this very truth demonstrated in today's lesson.

Jesus taught His followers to love everyone. You might be thinking, *That's a contradiction to today's lesson.* No, it is not. Loving and demonstrating kindness to those who do not follow God is possible without continually placing yourself in their company. It's a dangerous choice to become best buddies with those who do not seek and obey God. Make a decision today to be cautious when choosing your friends because the price you pay for being careless is too great.

Please understand that believers are called to go out into this world and be a light to the lost. In no way is this lesson intended to dispute this command. Missionaries go into ungodly environments every day because that is their calling from the Lord. Ministering to the lost and becoming best buddies with ungodly people are two different situations. You can reach the lost for Christ without compromising your spiritual condition. Stay in the Word of God, continually building up your spirit so that if temptation comes your way, you are strong enough to choose obedience.

That's enough for today. Let's review what you've learned:

- A righteous man is cautious in friendship.
- Ungodliness is contagious.
- Before the Israelites entered into the Promised Land, God commanded them to destroy all the people who lived there.
- God knew that if the people of Israel lived among ungodly people, they would become ungodly.
- Although you are to choose godly friends, you should demonstrate God's love to everyone, be a light to the lost, and pray for their salvation.

This week's memory verse is 1 John 3:15 (NT). It is written below. Say it to yourself three times.

"Anyone who hates his brother is a murderer, and you know that no murderer has eternal life in him."

15. Write this week's memory verse in the space provided.

_____

_____

_____

It's time to take Test 3.

Lesson 13

Friendships

In Lesson 12, you studied about the importance of choosing friends with caution. Once you have chosen a friend, how do you develop and strengthen that friendship? Below are three steps to doing this.

<u>Steps to Developing and Strengthening Friendships</u>

Step 1:   Spend time and communicate with that person.
Step 2:   Demonstrate God's love to him or her.
Step 3:   Respect him or her.

Just as you must spend time and communicate with God in order to develop and strengthen that relationship, you must also commit to spending time with people in order to develop friendships. Communication must be flowing between you as well.

According to Proverbs 17:17 (OT), **"A friend loves at all times."** Do you demonstrate God's love to your friends? That is the second step to developing and strengthening friendships. In Lesson 5, you read God's definition of love. Turning to 1 Corinthians 13:4-8a (NT), review this definition by reading it. Fill in the blanks below by writing your answers in the spaces provided.

1.   Love is _____ and _____.

2.   Love does not _____ or _____.

3.   Love is not _____, _____ or _____ - _____.

4.   Love is not easily _____ nor does it keep a record of

_____.

5. Love does not delight in _____, but it rejoices with the

_____.

6. Love always _____, _____, _____

and _____.

7. Love never _____.

Are you loving your friends according to God's definition of love? Perhaps you are thinking to yourself, *How could anyone live up to that kind of standard?* Don't despair. There's good news for you in Romans 5:5 (NT). Turn to this verse, and read it.

8. According to Romans 5:5 (NT), what has God poured into your heart by the Holy Spirit?

_____

You are capable of loving according to God's definition of love because He has poured His love into your heart. He did that when you accepted Jesus as your Lord and Savior. When you confessed your sins, prayed for God's forgiveness, and invited Jesus into your life, God poured His love into your heart by the Holy Spirit.

When you follow the steps outlined in Lesson 1 to develop and strengthen your relationship with God, His love inside you grows because your relationship with Him is deepening. As that relationship grows, you will be able to see others as He sees them. More importantly, you will be able to love others just as He loves them.

The third step to developing and strengthening a friendship is to respect one another. Following the Golden Rule is one way to show respect for another person. You'll remember from Lesson 7 that Jesus was the originator of the Golden Rule, "Do unto others as you would have them do unto you." Treat people the way you want to be treated. Respecting another person means showing kindness and consideration toward him or her.

In Ephesians 4:29-32 (NT), Paul penned an excellent definition of respecting others. Turning there, read these verses from the passage titled, "Living as Children of Light." Answer the questions below by placing a check mark beside the correct answer.

9. What should the words of your mouth accomplish? (Check all that are correct.)

    ____ a. They should be wholesome.
    ____ b. They should be helpful in building up others.
    ____ c. They should benefit others.

10. Of what should you rid yourself? (Check all that are correct.)

    ____ a. bitterness and rage
    ____ b. anger and brawling (or fighting)
    ____ c. slander and malice

11. What should you demonstrate toward others? (Check all that are correct.)

    ____ a. kindness
    ____ b. compassion
    ____ c. forgiveness

When you live according to God's definition of love and Paul's exhortation in Ephesians, you will strengthen your relationships with others and build strong, healthy friendships. That doesn't mean that disagreements won't ever arise. What should you do if you find yourself at odds with a friend? The first thing you should do is pray to God about the situation. Listen for His leading regarding it. Once you receive clear direction, talk to your friend about it. Listen to what he or she has to say with an open mind. Express your position without anger. Practice forgiveness. If the two of you can not resolve the matter, involve a godly mediator. A mediator is someone who is impartial toward the situation and able to give godly advice concerning it. This could be your youth leader at church or perhaps a parent. Friendships are valuable so don't just turn your back on a friend whenever conflict arises because love perseveres.

That's enough for today. Let's review what you've learned:

- The steps to developing and strengthening a friendship are: spending time and communicating with the individual, loving him or her and respecting him or her.
- According to God's Word, love is: patient, kind, rejoices with the truth, protects, trusts, hopes, and it perseveres.
- According to God's Word, love is not: envious, boastful, proud, rude, self-seeking or easily angered.
- Love does not keep a record of wrongs nor does it delight in evil.
- God pours His love into the heart of every believer, making it possible for him or her to love as God loves.
- A good friend lives by the Golden Rule, treating others as he or she desires to be treated.
- A good friend doesn't turn his or her back when conflict arises but perseveres through good times and bad.

This week's memory verse is 2 Peter 1:5-7 (NT). It is written below.

"For this very reason, make every effort to add to your faith goodness; and to goodness, knowledge; and to knowledge, self-control; and to self-control, perseverance; and to perseverance, godliness; and to godliness, brotherly kindness; and to brotherly kindness, love."

12. Write this week's memory verse in the space provided below. Say it to yourself three times.

_____

_____

_____

_____

_____

Lesson 14

Boy/Girl Relationships

In Lesson 13, you learned that a friend loves at all times. A friend must be patient and kind not jealous or boastful. Humility rather than pride is a characteristic of a true friend. Being rude or self-seeking is not acceptable in a friendship but putting others first is permissible. In a friendship, you must not become easily angered or keep a record of the times you've been hurt. Finding pleasure in evil is wrong, while seeking the truth is right. Protecting your friends at all times, you must be able to trust, hope and persevere through good times as well as bad. A true friendship will never fail no matter what comes along. When you develop and strengthen your relationship with God, He pours His love into your heart, making it possible for you to be the kind of friend He desires you to be.

As you can see, when you truly love someone, you are investing a great deal of yourself into that person. That is why you can not afford to choose your friends carelessly. God does not want to see you get hurt. When we don't choose our friends wisely, oftentimes we do get hurt. People who aren't seeking a deeper relationship with God do not love according to His definition. They are more likely to follow the world's standards, and the world says to *love yourself above others. Look out for number one because no one else will.* This is a very dangerous mind-set especially if you end up marrying someone who thinks like this.

Today's lesson addresses an issue that every young man and woman thinks about: dating, marriage and family. Most young adults agree that having a stable family life will be the single most important accomplishment in their lifetime. Sadly, the statistics show that many marriages across America are failing.

The Bible tells us that when God is our first love, He will meet our every need. He will provide the perfect partner for us. After all, marriage was His idea in the first place. He created Eve as a partner for Adam. They never got a divorce. They were perfect for each other. Unfortunately, they did not continue to put God first in their lives, and that cost them dearly in their relationship with Him as well as in their personal lives.

God makes us an offer we can't refuse. Love Me, obey Me, serve Me, and put Me first. Then, I will take care of all that concerns you. I will lead you down the right path and guide you in life's decisions. Let's look at some of God's many promises to lead and care for us when we put Him first. Look up each verse below, and fill in the blanks.

1. Deuteronomy 5:29 (OT): **"Oh, that their hearts would be inclined to fear me and _____ all my commands always, so that it might go well with them and their children forever!"**

2. Psalm 37:4 (OT): **"_____ yourself in the Lord and he will give you the desires of your heart."**

3. Proverbs 3:5-6 (OT): **"Trust in the Lord with all your heart and lean not on your _____ understanding; in all your ways _____ him, and he will make your paths straight."**

4. Jeremiah 7:23b (OT): **"_____ me, and I will be your God and you will be my people. _____ in all the ways I command you, that it may go well with you."**

5. Matthew 6:33 (NT): **"But seek _____ his kingdom and his righteousness, and all these things will be given to you as well."**

6. Romans 8:32 (NT): **"He who did not spare his own Son, but gave him up for us all—how will he not also, along with him, graciously _____ us all things?"**

7. Philippians 4:19 (NT): **"And my God will meet all your _____ according to His glorious riches in Christ Jesus."**

God desires that we love Him above any thing or person on the earth. When we do, He blesses us in every way. Pouring His Spirit into our hearts, God leads us into godly relationships or warns us when we are heading in the wrong direction. Many times people put their relationships with other people above their relationship with God. This is especially true when it comes to boy/girl relationships. When that happens, they ignore God's will for their lives. They get into wrong relationships, and many times they get hurt and hurt others, too. Everyone loses in this situation.

STOP FOR TODAY. FINISH LESSON NEXT TIME.

God's Word advises His children not to become involved with unbelievers. Turning in your Bible to 2 Corinthians 6:14 through 7:1 (NT), read this passage titled, "Do Not Be Yoked With Unbelievers." Answer the questions below by placing a check mark beside the correct answer.

8. Why should believers not become yoked, or involved, with un-believers? (Check all answers that are correct.)

   ____ a. because righteousness and wickedness have nothing in common

   ____ b. because light and darkness have no fellowship

   ____ c. because there is no harmony between Christ and Belial, who is Satan

9. As the temple of God, believers are to be _____ from the world.

   ____ a. united

   ____ b. separate

   ____ c. neither a or b

10. What does God promise to those who remain holy?

   ____ a. He promises to give them sons and daughters.

   ____ b. He promises to give them friends.

   ____ c. He promises to be their Father.

11. Why should believers purify themselves from everything that contaminates body and spirit? (Check all that are correct.)

   ____   a.   so they do not become contaminated
   ____   b.   out of reverence for God
   ____   c.   to impress other believers

Are you now convinced that you should not fellowship, or hang around with, unbelievers? You should be. Also, you should not be naive to the fact that not all Christians are seeking, serving and obeying God. It is important that you make sure that the person you are associating with really is who he or she claims to be. The Bible warns us that there are wolves in sheep's clothing. That's all the more reason to make sure you are in a right relationship with God so that you will be able to hear and to know His will for your life in the area of relationships.

You've learned a great deal about boy/girl relationships in this lesson. You're not finished. Realizing the dangers of dating is very important. Boys are physically attracted to girls, and girls are physically attracted to boys. When you put yourself in a position of being alone with someone of the opposite gender, you are putting yourself in a dangerous place. Temptation is bound to result. Temptation leads to sin, and sin separates you from God. When you are separated from God, you open the door to all kinds of trouble. So now you're thinking, *Are you saying I can't ever date?* Here's the deal. You can associate with members of the opposite gender without putting yourself in dangerous positions. Below are suggestions on how to do this:

- ✓ Do things as a group rather than as a couple.
- ✓ Talk about things other than love, romance or marriage.
- ✓ Talk honestly with your parents about your feelings.
- ✓ Don't do anything to cause someone else to sin.
- ✓ Devote your time to godly activities.[1]

Most importantly, put God first in your life. Pour your time, energy, and your love into Him. He loves you, and He wants you to be happy. When the time is right, He will provide that special someone—Mr. or Miss Right—and you will know it because you will be able to recognize God's voice!

---

[1] Joshua Harris, <u>I Kissed Dating Goodbye</u>, (Sisters, OR: Multnomah Publishers, Inc.), 111-132.

That's enough for today. Let's review what you've learned:

- In order to have successful relationships, you must put God first in your life.
- When you love and obey God, He will provide everything you need.
- God's Word warns believers not to marry unbelievers.
- In boy/girl relationships, avoid tempting situations.

This week's memory verse is 2 Peter 1:5-7 (NT). It is written below.

"For this very reason, make every effort to add to your faith goodness; and to goodness, knowledge; and to knowledge, self-control; and to self-control, perseverance; and to perseverance, godliness; and to godliness, brotherly kindness; and to brotherly kindness, love."

12. Write this week's memory verse in the space provided below. Say it to yourself three times.

_____

_____

_____

_____

_____

Lesson 15

The Character of a Godly Person

In Lesson 14, you studied about boy/girl relationships. You learned the importance of purity and godliness. Being godly in an ungodly world is not always easy, but it is always the right choice to make.

In Lesson 6, you studied about becoming God's friend. Being godly, or righteous, is a characteristic of God's friend. There are several verses in the Bible describing the characteristics of a godly, or righteous, person. In today's lesson, you'll study these characteristics and discover whether or not you fit the description of a godly young man or woman.

To discover the first characteristic of a godly individual, turn to and read Psalm 37:21 (OT). Answer the question below by writing your answer in the space provided.

1.   The wicked borrow and don't repay, but those who are godly (or righteous) do what?

_____

Godly people give generously to others. In other words, a godly person is a <u>selfless</u> person and not a selfish person. A <u>selfless</u> person puts the needs of others first. Humility is another word for selflessness. A selfish person puts his or her own needs first. "Pride" is another word for selfishness.

The first characteristic of a righteous, or godly, person is that he or she gives freely to others. What else does God's Word say about godly people? Skip down a few verses to 30-31. Read them, and answer the following questions.

2.   What does the righteous man speak?

_____

3.   What is in the heart of a righteous man?

_____

A righteous man or woman speaks words of wisdom—what is just. Discussing subjects that God would want you to talk about is one way to speak words of wisdom. When you're talking to another person, imagine that Jesus is in the room. Don't say anything to that person that you wouldn't say in front of Jesus. Talking negative about others is not acceptable. Always be honest (or just) because that is also a characteristic of a righteous person.

According to Psalm 37:31 (OT), God's law is in the heart of a righteous man or woman. God's law, or Word, is so powerful. When you hide it in your heart, it strengthens you so that you don't fall into sin. That's what verse 31 means when it says, **"…his feet do not slip."**

Below are more verses describing the characteristics of the righteous. Look up each verse. Read it. Match the columns below by writing the letter of the Bible verse on the left in the blank provided before each corresponding characteristic listed on the right.

<u>Bible Verse</u>   **<u>Characteristic of the Godly</u>**

a. Psalm 15:1-2 (OT)   ___ **4.** Praises God and lives before Him.

b. Psalm 15:3 (OT)   ___ **5.** Doesn't slander or do wrong to others.

c. Psalm 15:4b (OT)   ___ **6.** Cares for his animals.

d. Psalm 140:13 (OT)   ___ **7.** His words nourish, or help, others.

e. Proverbs 10:21 (OT)   ___ **8.** Keeps his oath even when it hurts.

f. Proverbs 10:32 (OT)   ___ **9.** His walk is blameless, and he does what is right.

g. Proverbs 12:10 (OT)   ___ **10.** Knows what is fitting to say.

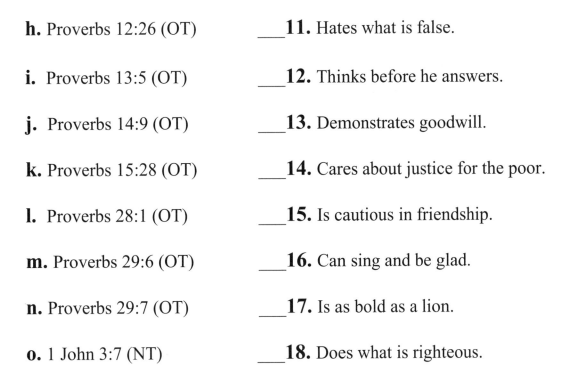

h. Proverbs 12:26 (OT)   ___**11.** Hates what is false.

i. Proverbs 13:5 (OT)   ___**12.** Thinks before he answers.

j. Proverbs 14:9 (OT)   ___**13.** Demonstrates goodwill.

k. Proverbs 15:28 (OT)   ___**14.** Cares about justice for the poor.

l. Proverbs 28:1 (OT)   ___**15.** Is cautious in friendship.

m. Proverbs 29:6 (OT)   ___**16.** Can sing and be glad.

n. Proverbs 29:7 (OT)   ___**17.** Is as bold as a lion.

o. 1 John 3:7 (NT)   ___**18.** Does what is righteous.

Do these characteristics describe you? Reading through them again, give an honest assessment as to whether or not you measure up to these characteristics. If you fall short, don't feel defeated. Pray and ask God to help you choose righteousness. Stay in His Word, pray and praise Him. Over time, He will mold you into the righteous young man or woman He desires you to become.

One of the characteristics of a godly person is that he or she is as bold as a lion. If you are godly, you don't need to be fearful because God is on your side. Throughout the Bible, God protects the righteous. He hears and answers their prayers. According to Romans 8:31 (NT), if God is on your side, who can be against you? If you are righteous, you don't need to fear people. Who can stand against God? God is your protector if you are righteous.

Demonstrating goodwill is yet another characteristic of the righteous. In other words, you care about the well-being of others. You must care about the well-being of unbelievers as well as believers. Although you should not closely fellowship with unbelievers, it is your responsibility to care about them and to share God's love with them. Show kindness to them, help them when you can, and pray for their salvation. After all, winning the lost is another characteristic of a godly person.

That's enough for today. Let's review what you've learned:

- Characteristics of a righteous person include:
  Giving generously, speaking wisdom and what is just and keeping God's law in your heart.
- Other characteristics of a righteous person include:
  Praising God and living before Him, not slandering or doing wrong to others, caring for the needs of animals, nourishing others with words, keeping oaths even when it hurts, speaking truth from the heart, knowing what is fitting to say, hating what is false, thinking before answering, demonstrating goodwill, caring about the poor, being cautious in friendship, singing and being glad, being as bold as a lion, and doing what is right.

This week's memory verse is 2 Peter 1:5-7 (NT). It is written below.

"For this very reason, make every effort to add to your faith goodness; and to goodness, knowledge; and to knowledge, self-control; and to self-control, perseverance; and to perseverance, godliness; and to godliness, brotherly kindness; and to brotherly kindness, love."

19. Write this week's memory verse in the space provided below. Say it to yourself three times.

_____

_____

_____

_____

Lesson 16

Being Godly in an Ungodly World

Congratulations! You've made it to the last lesson of this study, *Godly Relationships*. Discovering the importance of developing and maintaining your relationship with God, you have learned a great deal. Abiding in God's Word, prayer and praise are all elements of strengthening your relationship with Him. When your relationship with God is strong, other relationships in your life will be strengthened as well.

Hopefully, you have learned the importance that obedience and respect play in your relationships with others. Discovering the importance of choosing your friends wisely, you now realize that demonstrating God's love to everyone around you is a command from God. When it comes to boy/girl relationships, you read that God's Word warns believers not to be unequally yoked with unbelievers. Lastly, you have studied about the characteristics of a godly person. In Lesson 15, you had the opportunity to measure yourself against these characteristics to see if you fit the description of a godly or righteous young man or woman.

In 2 Timothy 3:1-5 (NT), the Bible warns that in the last days, people who belong to the world will become increasingly ungodly. Turning to these verses, read them from the passage titled, "Godlessness in the Last Days." Answer the questions that follow by writing your answers in the spaces provided.

1.   Describe the character of ungodly people in the last days:

_____

_____

_____

_____

_____

_____

2. What does Paul say about our fellowship with these people?

_____

These are the last days. It is of the utmost importance that you remain close to God in these days, and you don't turn to the left or to the right of His commands. Certainly, temptations will come. If you will trust and obey God, He will see you through every situation. Paul wrote about this very subject in 1 Corinthians 10:12-13 (NT). Turning there, read these verses. Answer the questions below by writing your answers in the spaces provided.

3. According to verse 12, why should you be careful even though you are standing firm?

_____

4. In verse 13, what two things will God do for you when you are tempted?

_____

_____

_____

_____

God will not let you be tempted beyond what you can bear, but He will make a way for you to escape temptation if you trust and obey Him.

In the book of Revelation, John penned letters on behalf of Jesus to seven churches. In several of these letters, John condemned believers for turning away from God. In Revelation 2:4 (NT), Jesus accused the church at Ephesus of a very dangerous act. Turning there, read that verse.

5. Write Revelation 2:4 (NT) in the space provided below.

_____

_____

"You have forsaken your first love." Being godly in an ungodly world comes down to this very principle, **Make God your first love.** Never allow someone or some thing to take His place. How do you make God your first love? First of all, you develop and strengthen your relationship with Him through the steps you learned in Lesson 1. They are:

Steps to developing and strengthening your relationship with God:

Step 1: Spending time with God through:
a. Studying, meditating and confessing His Word;
b. Communicating with Him through prayer;
c. Praising Him.

Step 2: Loving Him with all your heart, soul and mind.

Step 3: Obeying Him.

By allowing God's priorities to be your priorities, you make Him your first love. Expressing God's love to others through your kind words and deeds and looking for opportunities to serve others are ways in which you can demonstrate that God is your first love. When you make God your first love, you hate what is evil, flee from ungodliness and choose godliness in all areas of your life.

Unless you are godly, you cannot succeed in developing and strengthening your relationship with God or with others. Being godly in an ungodly world is not easy. However, it is the only way to experience true peace and satisfaction in your life. The things this world has to offer cannot compare to what God has for those who love and obey Him. Make a decision right here and now to choose godliness. All you have to lose is misery and destruction, but you have everything to gain. What will it be?

That's enough for today. Let's review what you've learned:

- In the last days, people will become increasingly ungodly.
- If you continue to love and obey God, He will deliver you from temptation and sin.
- Making God your first love is the way to remain godly.
- Unless you are godly, you cannot be successful in developing and strengthening godly relationships with God or with others.

This week's memory verse is 2 Peter 1:5-7 (NT). It is written below.

"For this very reason, make every effort to add to your faith goodness; and to goodness, knowledge; and to knowledge, self-control; and to self-control, perseverance; and to perseverance, godliness; and to godliness, brotherly kindness; and to brotherly kindness, love."

6.   Write this week's memory verse in the space provided below. Say it to yourself three times.

_____

_____

_____

_____

Congratulations! You've completed this study, *Godly Relationships*. Don't stop here. Continue in God's Word, and remember, Jesus said, **"I no longer call you servants, because a servant does not know his master's business. Instead, I have called you friends, for everything that I learned from my Father I have made known to you"** (John 15:15).

It's time to take Test 4.

Test 1

Lessons 1-4

Short Answer Questions: Write your answers in the spaces provided.

1-3.   According to the Bible, list three reasons why God created man.

1.   _____

2.   _____

3.   _____

4-6.   List the three steps to developing and strengthening a relationship with God.

4.   _____

5.   _____

6.   _____

True/False Questions: Put a "T" in front of those statements that are true. Put an "F" in front of those statements that are false.

____   7.   Jesus is referred to as the "Word" in the Bible.

____   8.   God created Jesus just before He was sent to earth.

____   9.   Jesus said that if you obey His commands, you'll remain in His love.

____   10.   In John 15, Jesus refers to Himself as the "gardener" and to believers as the "fruit."

____   11.   Jesus taught His followers how to pray.

____   12.   When you pray, honor God's name, pray His kingdom come in your life, and ask Him to supply your daily needs.

____   13.   God does not require that you forgive others in order to receive His forgiveness.

____   14.   When you pray, ask God to lead you away from temptation.

_____ 15.   Prayer is one-way communication.

Multiple-Choice Questions: Put a check mark beside the correct answer.

16.   The Psalmist wrote to enter God's gates and courts with:

_____   a.   thanksgiving
_____   b.   praise
_____   c.   both a and b

17.   In the Old Testament, God dwelt in which area of the temple?

_____   a.   outer courtyard
_____   b.   Holy Place
_____   c.   Most Holy Place

18.   What happened at the temple when Jesus died on the cross?

_____   a.   they got new curtains
_____   b.   the curtains fell down
_____   c.   the curtains tore in two

19.   All of the methods of praising God listed in Lesson 4 were found in which book of the Bible?

_____   a.   Song of Solomon
_____   b.   Psalms
_____   c.   Proverbs

20.   What can you experience through praise and worship?

_____   a.   an improved singing voice
_____   b.   God's favor
_____   c.   God's presence

21.   Write this week's memory verse and its address in the space provided below.

_____

_____

_____

_____

Test 2

Lessons 5-8

Short Answer Questions: Write your answers in the spaces provided.

List the two greatest commandments according to Jesus.

1. _____

2. _____

In 1 Corinthians 13:4-8a, God's definition of love is revealed. In the space below, write what love is and is not according to this passage.

3-5. _____

_____

_____

True/False Questions: Put a "T" in front of those statements that are true. Put an "F" in front of those statements that are false.

____ 6. God entered into covenant relationships with Noah, Abram and David.

____ 7. God did not consider the spiritual condition of the men with whom He entered into covenant.

____ 8. Psalm 15 describes the characteristics of someone with whom God would call "friend."

____ 9. Righteousness is a very important characteristic of a person God calls "friend."

____ 10. God promises that things will go well for the individual who obeys Him and walks in the ways He commands.

____ 11. In the Old Testament, God gave His commandments to Israel through a man named Solomon.

____ 12. The Ten Commandments are the only commandments God gave to Israel.

____ 13. Jesus came to abolish (do away with) the Old Testament commandments.

71

_____ 14. The Golden Rules says, "Do unto others as you would have them do unto you."

_____ 15. The more obedient you are to God, the more He reveals Himself to you.

Multiple-Choice Questions: Put a check mark beside the correct answer.

16. What is the key to having a successful relationship with God?

     _____ a. obedience
     _____ b. having a good reputation
     _____ c. being able to make a lot of money

17. What did Abram give Melchizedek after he captured Lot from the hand of the enemy?

     _____ a. a blessing
     _____ b. a tithe
     _____ c. Lot

18. What does the name "Melchizedek" mean?

     _____ a. king of peace
     _____ b. king of righteousness
     _____ c. both a and b

19. In the Old Testament, God accused Israel of doing what?

     _____ a. not recognizing Melchizedek
     _____ b. robbing Him
     _____ c. robbing other people

20. According to Jesus, what is difficult for a rich man to do?

     _____ a. enter into heaven
     _____ b. give to charities
     _____ c. make sacrifices

21. Write this week's memory verse as well as its address in the space provided below.

_____

_____

_____

Test 3

Lessons 9-12

Short Answer Questions: Write your answers in the spaces provided.

From the Bible give three examples of Jesus obeying or caring for His parents or mother?

1. _____

2. _____

3. _____

4. Who was the disciple Jesus asked to care for Mary after His death? _____

5-7. List the three sibling relationships you studied about in Lesson 10.

5. _____

6. _____

7. _____

8. What was at the core of the problem between the siblings you listed previously?

   _____

9. List one of the punishments God allowed because of jealousy between siblings (Cain or Miriam's punishment).

   _____

10. Why is jealousy so dangerous? _____

   _____

True/False Questions: Put a "T" in front of those statements that are true. Put an "F" in front of those statements that are false.

____ 11. Hebrews 13:17 says to obey the leaders in your life.

____ 12. Leaders do not have to answer to God for anything.

____ 13. God establishes authorities on the earth.

____ 14. When you rebel against authority, you are rebelling against God.

____ 15. Paying taxes is an option, not a requirement.

____ 16. A righteous man is careless in friendship.

____ 17. Ungodliness is not contagious.

____ 18. God commanded Israel to destroy the inhabitants before they entered into the Promised Land.

____ 19. Israel obeyed God and destroyed the inhabitants of the land.

____ 20. In order to demonstrate God's love to a lost world, you should become good friends with the ungodly.

21. Write this week's memory verse as well as where it is found in the space below.

_____

_____

_____

_____

Test 4

Lessons 13-16

Short Answer Questions: Write your answers in the spaces provided.

List the three steps to developing and strengthening a relationship.

1. _____

2. _____

3. _____

4. Why is it possible for you to love according to God's definition?

   _____

5. What rule should you follow when relating to others?_____

True/False Questions: Put a "T" in front of those statements that are true. Put an "F" in front of those statements that are false.

___ 6. The most important relationship in your life will be with the person you marry.

___ 7. The Bible warns believers not to be yoked with unbelievers.

___ 8. It's dangerous to associate or become friends with the wrong people.

___ 9. When you put God first in your life, He will take care of your every need.

___ 10. In a boy/girl relationship, avoid tempting situations.

Short Answer: Write your answers to the following question in the spaces provided.

List five characteristics of a righteous or godly person.

11. _____

12. _____

13. _____

14. _____

15. _____

Multiple-Choice Questions: Put a check mark beside the correct answer.

16. What is the first step to developing and maintaining a relationship with God?

    ____ a.   following the Golden Rule
    ____ b.   spending time with Him
    ____ c.   making your relationship with other people top priority

17. What is the second step to developing and strengthening your relationship with God?

    ____ a.   spending time with Him
    ____ b.   loving Him
    ____ c.   obeying Him

18. What did Jesus have against the church of Ephesus?

    ____ a.   They had forsaken their first love.
    ____ b.   They had forsaken the assembling of themselves together.
    ____ c.   They had forsaken each other.

19. What is the third step to developing and strengthening your relationship with God?

    ____ a.   spending time with Him
    ____ b.   loving Him
    ____ c.   obeying Him

20. How do you make God your first love? (Check all answers that are correct.)

    ____ a.   by developing and strengthening your relationship with Him
    ____ b.   by making His priorities your priorities
    ____ c.   choosing to be godly in an ungodly world

21. Write this week's memory verse and its address in the space provided below.

_____

_____

_____

_____

Answer Key

Lesson 1:

1. A relationship is a connection between two or more parties who share a common bond.
2. God created man to have children, fill the earth, subdue it and rule over it. He created him to rule over the fish, birds and all creatures.
3. God created man to care for the earth.
4. God created man for His glory.
5. God created man to do good works.
6. God created man for Himself.

7. "You are worthy, our Lord and God, to receive glory and honor and power, for you created all things, and by your will they were created and have their being."

Lesson 2:

1. T; 2.T; 3.T; 4.T; 5.F; 6.T; 7.T; 8.F; 9.T; 10.T; 11.T; 12.T; 13.T; 14.F; 15.F; 16.T;
17. T; 18.F; 19.T; 20.T

21. "You are worthy, our Lord and God, to receive glory and honor and power, for you created all things, and by your will they were created and have their being."

Lesson 3:

1. These words should honor God.
2. He meant that His will be done on earth and in the lives of people.
3. Our daily bread
4. Our sins. Your forgiveness of others is related to God's forgiveness toward you.
5. "And lead us not into temptation."
6. "Then the Father will give you whatever you ask in my name."
7. "You are worthy, our Lord and God, to receive glory and honor and power, for you created all things, and by your will they were created and have their being."

Lesson 4:

1. Worship, come
2. Enter, praise, praise
3. c; 4.a; 5.g; 6.e; 7.d; 8.f; 9.b

10. "You are worthy, our Lord and God, to receive glory and honor and power, for you created all things, and by your will they were created and have their being."

Test 1: (#1-20 worth 4.75 points; #21 worth 5 points)

1-3. God created man to have children; inhabit, care for and take dominion over the earth and everything in it; to glorify Him; to do good works, and for His sake.

4-6. The three steps to developing and strengthening a relationship with God are: spending time with Him, loving Him and obeying Him.

7. T; 8.F; 9.T; 10.F; 11.T; 12.T; 13.F; 14.T; 15.F; 16.c; 17.c; 18.c; 19.b; 20.c

21. "You are worthy, our Lord and God, to receive glory and honor and power, for you created all things, and by your will they were created and have their being." Revelation 4:11

Lesson 5:

1. a; 2.b; 3.c; 4.a

5. Love is patient and kind. It does not envy or brag, and it isn't rude. It is not selfish or easily angered. It keeps no record of wrongs and does not delight in evil but rejoices in truth. It always protects, trusts, hopes and perseveres. Love never fails.
6. Obey Him.
7. "But I gave them this command: Obey me, and I will be your God and you will be my people. Walk in all the ways I command you, that it may go well with you."

Lesson 6:

1. Noah was righteous and blameless among the people of his time. He walked with God.

2. a,b,c,d; 3.b,c;

4. blameless, righteous, truth, slander, wrong, slur, despises, honors, keeps, lends, bribe, shaken
5. "But I gave them this command: Obey me, and I will be your God and you will be my people. Walk in all the ways I command you, that it may go well with you."

Lesson 7:

1. gods	5. Honor	9. false	13. least
2. idol, bow	6. murder	10. covet	14. great
3. name	7. adultery	11. abolish	
4. holy	8. steal	12. Disappear	

15. "So in everything, do to others what you would have them do to you, for this sums up the Law and the Prophets."

16. "Whoever has my commands and obeys them, he is the one who loves me. He who loves me will be loved by my Father, and I too will love him and show myself to him."

17. "But I gave them this command: Obey me, and I will be your God and you will be my people. Walk in all the ways I command you, that it may go well with you."

Lesson 8:

1. 318
2. yes
3. all the goods, Lot's possessions, the women and the other people
4. king of Sodom and Melchizadek, king of Salem
5. a priest of God Most High
6. a tenth of everything
7. king of righteousness and king of peace
8. He had none.
9. He was without beginning and end.
10. Jesus, Son of God
11. T; 12.F; 13.T; 14.T; 15.T; 16.T; 17.T; 18.T; 19.F; 20.T; 21.T; 22.T;

23. "But I gave them this command: Obey me, and I will be your God and you will be my people. Walk in all the ways I command you, that it may go well with you."

Test 2: (#1-20 worth 4.75 points; #21 worth 5 points)

1. Love the Lord your God with all your heart, soul and mind.
2. Love your neighbor as yourself.
3-5. Love is patient and kind. It does not envy or boast. It is not proud, rude or self-seeking. It is not easily angered. It keeps no record of wrongs. It does not delight in evil but rejoices with the truth. It always protects, trusts, hopes and perseveres. Love never fails.

6. T; 7.F; 8.T; 9.T; 10.T; 11.F; 12.F; 13.F; 14.T; 15.T; 16.a; 17.b; 18.c; 19.b; 20.a;

21. "But I gave them this command: Obey me, and I will be your God and you will be my people. Walk in all the ways I command you, that it may go well with you." Jeremiah 7:23

Lesson 9:

1. d; 2.a; 3.b; 4.c
5. obedient
6. God

7. T; 8.F; 9.T; 10.T; 11.F; 12.T; 13.F; 14.T

15.	"Dear woman, here is your son." "Here is your mother."

16.	"Anyone who hates his brother is a murderer, and you know that no murderer has eternal life in him."

Lesson 10:

1.	T; 2.T; 3.F; 4.T; 5.T; 6.F; 7.T; 8.T; 9.T; 10.T; 11.F; 12.T; 13.T; 14.F; 15.F;

16.	"Anyone who hates his brother is a murderer, and you know that no murderer has eternal life in him."

Lesson 11:

1.	You should obey your leaders.
2.	Any answer is acceptable.
3.	The Lord is in control of it.
4.	authorities; 5. rebel; 6. punishment; 7. servants; 8. conscience; 9. taxes;
10.	Respect

11.	"Anyone who hates his brother is a murderer, and you know that no murderer has eternal life in him."

Lesson 12:

1.	a; 2.c; 3.b; 4.a,b,c,d; 5.a,b,c; 6.a,b,c,d; 7.c; 8.a; 9.a,b,c,d; 10.a,b; 11.c; 12.b, 13.b;
14.	c;

15.	"Anyone who hates his brother is a murderer, and you know that no murderer has eternal life in him."

Test 3: (#1-20 worth 4.75 points; #21 worth 5 points)

1.	He obeyed them after returning home from having stayed behind in Jerusalem.
2.	He obeyed Mary at the wedding when He changed the water into wine.
3.	He cared for Mary while on the cross when He asked John to care for her after His death.
4.	John
5.	Cain and Abel
6.	Joseph and his siblings
7.	Moses and his siblings
8.	jealousy
9.	Cain was forced to be a wanderer and could not garden. Miriam was stricken with leprosy.
10.	It opens the door to disorder and every evil practice.

11.   T; 12.F; 13.T; 14.T; 15.F; 16.F; 17.F; 18.T; 19.F; 20.F;

21.   "Anyone who hates his brother is a murderer, and you know that no murderer has eternal life in him." 1 John 3:15

Lesson 13:

1.	patient, kind	5.	evil, truth
2.	envy, boast	6.	protects, trusts, hopes, perseveres
3.	proud, rude, self-seeking	7.	fails
4.	angered, wrongs		

8.   God has poured out His love into your heart by the Holy Spirit.

9.   a,b,c; 10.a,b,c; 11.a,b,c;

12.   "For this very reason, make every effort to add to your faith goodness; and to goodness, knowledge; and to knowledge, self-control; and to self-control, perseverance; and to perseverance, godliness; and to godliness, brotherly kindness; and to brotherly kindness, love."

Lesson 14:

1.	keep	5.	first
2.	Delight	6.	give
3.	own, acknowledge	7.	needs
4.	Obey, Walk	8.	a,b,c; 9.b; 10.c;11.a,b;

12.   "For this very reason, make every effort to add to your faith goodness; and to goodness, knowledge; and to knowledge, self-control; and to self-control, perseverance; and to perseverance, godliness; and to godliness, brotherly kindness; and to brotherly kindness, love."

Lesson 15:

1.   They give generously.
2.   He speaks wisdom and what is just.
3.   The law of God is in his heart.
4.   d; 5.b; 6.g; 7.e; 8.c; 9.a; 10.f; 11.i; 12.k; 13.j; 14.n; 15.h; 16.m; 17.l; 18.o;

19.   "For this very reason, make every effort to add to your faith goodness; and to goodness, knowledge; and to knowledge, self-control; and to self-control, perseverance; and to perseverance, godliness; and to godliness, brotherly kindness; and to brotherly kindness, love."

Lesson 16:

1. They'll be lovers of themselves and money. They'll be boastful, proud, abusive, disobedient to their parents, ungrateful, unholy, without love, unforgiving, slanderous, without self-control, brutal, not lovers of good, treacherous, rash, conceited, lovers of pleasure rather than lovers of God—having a form of godliness but denying its power.

2. Have nothing to do with them.

3. You might fall.

4. He will not let you be tempted beyond what you can bear. When you are tempted, He'll provide a way out so you can stand up under it.

5. "Yet I hold this against you: You have forsaken your first love."

6. "For this very reason, make every effort to add to your faith goodness; and to goodness, knowledge; and to knowledge, self-control; and to self-control, perseverance; and to perseverance, godliness; and to godliness, brotherly kindness; and to brotherly kindness, love."

Test 4: (#1-20 worth 4.75 points; #21 worth 5 points)

1. spending time with him/her
2. loving him/her
3. respecting him/her
4. because God has poured His love into the heart of every believer
5. the Golden Rule
6. F; 7.T; 8.T; 9.T; 10.T;

11-15.
He/she gives generously, speaks wisdom and what is just, keeps God's law in his/her heart, praises God and lives before Him, doesn't slander or do wrong to others, cares for the needs of animals, nourishes others with words, keeps oaths even when it hurts, speaks truth from the heart, knows what is fitting to say, hates what is false, thinks before answering, demonstrates goodwill, cares about the poor, is cautious in friendship, sings and is glad, is as bold as a lion and does what is right.

16. b; 17.b; 18.a; 19.c; 20;a,b,c;

21. "For this very reason, make every effort to add to your faith goodness; and to goodness, knowledge; and to knowledge, self-control; and to self-control, perseverance; and to perseverance, godliness; and to godliness, brotherly kindness; and to brotherly kindness, love." 2 Peter 1:5-7